ONE HUNDRED YEARS OF RIOJA ALTA

1890-1990

2nd Edition, Revised & Updated

La Rioja Alta, S.A.

BODEGAS FUNDADAS EN 1890

Published by: LA RIOJA ALTA, S.A.
Edition: LA RIOJA ALTA, S.A.
Photography: SIGFRIDO KOCH
Text: MANUEL RUIZ HERNANDEZ
English translation: BRIAN WEBSTER with EUROPVIN, S. A.
(SUSAN O'CONNELL and CHRISTOPHER CANNAN)
Design: FELIX GARRIDO
Illustrations: ARRAITZ KOCH ELIZEGI
Photomechanics: LAR, S.A.
Photocomposition: GROS
Printed by: AIALDE, S.A.
Binding: BOEL
I.S.B.N.: 84 - 404-7027-4
D. L.: S. S. 405-90

ONE HUNDRED YEARS OF RIOJA ALTA

1890-1990

DISEÑO DE LA MARCA.

MARCA CONCEDIDA

La Rioja Alta

SOCIEDAD DE COSECHEROS DE VINO

Haro

(Escala variable).

Madrid 30 de Diciembre de 1916.

E. MORALES FUENCARRAL.74. PRAL.MADRID

De la "Asociación Española de Agentes de Propiedad Industrial"

"Viña Alberdi" estate in Rodenzo (22 Ha.).

8

DESCRIPCIÓN DE LA MARCA.

Consiste en una etiqueta en cuya parte superior central va la marca consistente en un paisaje en el centro del cual hay un rio sobre cuya superficie se leen las palabras "Rio Oja".

En la margen izquierda de dicho rio se ven tres arboles y un arbusto, y en la derecha un árbol, estando bordeada esta última margen por varias piedras, saliendo de la juntura de dos de ellas un arbusto que se inclina hacia el rio. Debajo de dicho paisaje se leen las palabras "Marca concedida".

A continuación está inscrito el nombre de la Sociedad con caracteres de letra redondilla francesa "La Rioja Alta", debajo del cual se lee "Sociedad de Cosecheros de vino", y en la parte inferior, a la derecha, la inscripción del pueblo donde radican las bodegas o sea "Haro".

Sirve para distinguir vinos.

Se empleará aplicandola por cualquier procedimiento a los envases de los mismos sin distinción de tamaños, tipos de letra y colores.

Madrid 30 de Diciembre de 1916.

E. Morales

Open letter to whoever occupies the Presidency on the commemoration of the Second Centenary

Dear Friend,

I am writing this letter to you, at the end of our first hundred years, despite the fact that by the time it reaches you, another hundred years will have elapsed.

I would like to tell you about some of the things we have done during this long period of time and conclude by conveying a message which I should like to send you as we cross the threshold of this first century.

During the first fifty or sixty years of our existence we established and developed a long term policy of outstanding quality. This was reflected in an order for 3,500 Bordeaux casks made shortly after the company was founded.

During the last four decades, having overcome the difficulties endured in the war years, we have continued to develop, in accordance with our motto of "quality first". We have also extended our activities to vinegrowing, having initiated production in several important vineyards.

We have seen this development, this constant and unique line of action, as a return to our original principles, faithful to a tradition which has been handed down to us.

In an age when, in order to praise the wines of Rioja, it was fashionable to use terms such as "light" "young", "fruity", we continued, against the general trend, rediscovering our origins by ageing wines according to tradition and, therefore, the initial methods.

In this way we have developed throughout our one hundred years of existence, driven by an obsession for improving the quality of our wines.

Today, there is a group of bodegas in the Rioja which, like us, are involved in a constant search for excellence and a struggle to make full use of the potential quality which our grapes contain. It is necessary for many more to become enthusiastic about this idea. Only then will La Rioja have found the way to take its place among the foremost wine-producing areas of the world.

By the time this letter reaches you, many things will have happened. Currently we are all awaiting the miracles of 1992 and the Single European Market. This will seem a triviality to you, firmly established, as you may be, in the "United States of Europe".

Let's not speak of technology. Sometimes I do not know if I can believe or even dream that you will make use of artificial sight, giving orders to robots, in operations such as racking, in which it is so important to achieve good results. Even in the grape harvest, although I do not quite see how you will be able to transmit to the robots the pride and care these tasks require.

I have set aside this copy of the book which we have published to commemorate this date and with great pleasure dedicate it to the many friends we are fortunate enough to have.

I sincerely hope that on the celebration of the second centenary, you will continue to work with the same enthusiasm, interest and commitment to quality that has always guided us and which continues to provide us with a source of motivation. This is the message I mentioned at the beginning of this letter.

My best wishes,

Guillermo de Aranzabal Alberdi

BOARD OF DIRECTORS IN 1890

Chairman:	Daniel-Alfredo Ardanza Sánchez
Members:	Dionisio del Prado Lablanca
	Saturnina García-Cid Gárate
	Mariano Lacort y Tapia
	Felipe Puig de la Bellacasa y Herrán
Managing Director:	Mariano Lacort y Tapia

BOARD OF DIRECTORS IN 1990

Chairman:	Guillermo de Aranzabal Alberdi
Vice Chairman:	José María de Arana y Aizpurua
Secretary:	José Miguel Rezola García-Avecilla
Members:	Ignacio de Aranzabal Alberdi
	José Alfredo Ardanza Trevijano
	Gonzalo Artiach Meda
	Guillermo Galdos Egaña
	José Ramón Herrero-Fontana
	Luis Knoerr Barandiarán
	Fernando Maguregui Palomo
	Pedro Masaveu Peterson
	Ramón Peironcely Aguirrebengoa
	Nicolás Salterain Elgoibar
Managing Director:	Guillermo de Aranzabal Agudo
	Jaime Ramón Usatorre Zubillaga

Contents

Introduction

FOR many years LA RIOJA ALTA, S.A., has endeavoured to help its friends and clients extend their knowledge of all factors which affect the preparation and ageing of wines.

With this idea in mind, we began to publish installments of "VENDIMIA" in 1979, on which this book, "ONE HUNDRED YEARS OF RIOJA ALTA", is based, and which we now present.
Manuel Ruiz Hernández has revised and extended his original texts and Sigfrido Koch has given a touch of poetry and tenderness to a brilliant dissertation on the science of wine-making.

"Tannins", "polyphenols", "malolactic", "aftertaste" are words which are used commonly today among lovers of good wine; everyone would like to know the real significance and importance of these words.

Wine is not manufactured, it is aged. It is a product which is born, grows and moves just like all living beings. Its ability to evolve is what makes it enormously attractive and different from practically all other gastronomic and alcohol-based products. All these circumstances, together with the appreciation of enthusiasts for the care and love which goes into each bottle of wine, means that it is not enough for wine-tasters just to taste a good "Reserva", but also to be familiar with all the aspects which, in different ways and at different times, affect the birth and evolution of good Rioja wine.

Today, enthusiasts of Rioja not only need to drink good Rioja wine, but "experience" it at the same time, know how it has evolved and what processes have influenced its development. How it has been treated and prepared.

Our intention has not been just to create a technical book to commemorate our centenary, but also, and especially, to disseminate the art and technology of Rioja so that the lovers of the wines can gain a basic knowledge, which afterwards will be augmented by the individual sensibility of a person who has a glass of good wine before him.

We hope that, by means of this study, which is full of science and poetry, we have contributed a little more to the knowledge of wine-making.

THE SOIL

Vines are grown in several different soil types in the Rioja. There are many, but the most important are three in number: marl, ferrous clays and alluvial soils.

When one enters La Rioja, as does the River Ebro, through the rocky gorge "Las Conchas de Haro", on the left one can see vineyards which grow on yellowish, ochre-coloured soils, on terraces which descend from the Sierra Cantabria to the Ebro. This is the Rioja Alavesa and the soil is marl. Opposite, on one's right, squat, rounded hills and valleys. The valleys are formed by the rivers Oja, Najerilla, Iregua, Leza and Cidacos. On the flat, open land beside these rivers, are vineyards. The soil is alluvial. The reddish slopes which bord these open expanses, are made up largely of ferrous clay soil.

These soils are outlined on the following map. We have tried to imitate the colour of these soils: ochre or light sienna represents marl; the reddish colour, the alluvial soils; we have rendered the ferrous clay soils with brown.

We could even distinguish another ten types of soils, but these are of lesser importance from the viticultural point of view and are not coloured on this map.

The soil-type is distinguished, not only by the colour and the relief of the land - terraced, ridged or flat - but also by its internal structure, clay, sand, rock, stones, etc., so that the development of the root, its growth and expansion, is conditioned by these factors.

Let us imagine how these roots grow in the soil. In yellowish-ochre marl soils, once the "barbado" (or rooted vine) has been planted, it grows roots which progressively extend and deepen until, when they have reached a depth of about one metre, they come across the first disintegrated rock. Only a little lower down, there is compact rock. The roots penetrate easily between the disintegrated rock and look for cracks in the compact rock in order to continue growing downwards. They often find a crack and the root itself, when it thickens inside this crack, increases the size of the cavity. The contact between the roots and the rock does not harm the plant.

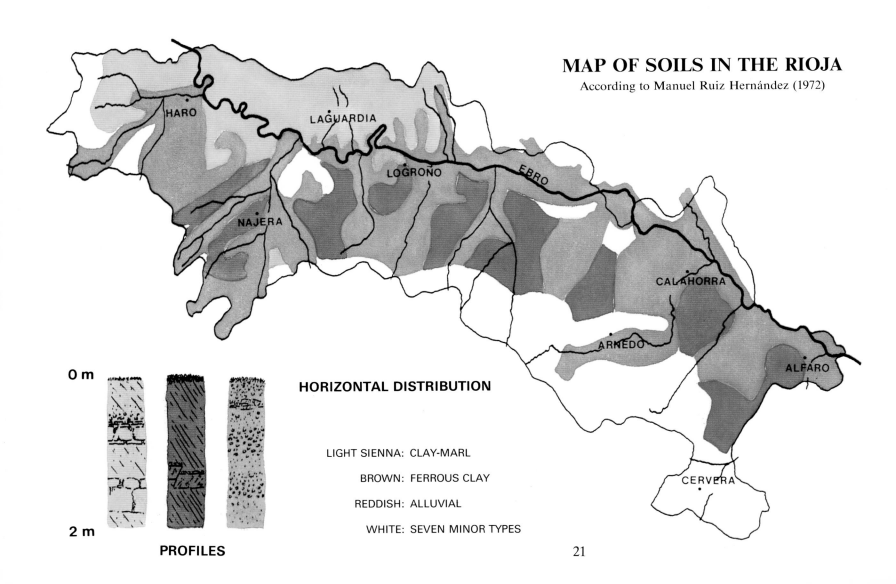

MAP OF SOILS IN THE RIOJA
According to Manuel Ruiz Hernández (1972)

0 m

2 m

PROFILES

HORIZONTAL DISTRIBUTION

LIGHT SIENNA: CLAY-MARL

BROWN: FERROUS CLAY

REDDISH: ALLUVIAL

WHITE: SEVEN MINOR TYPES

21

In reddish, ferrous clay soils, once the vine has been planted, the development and penetration of the root is slow; this soil is compact, and very clayey. The possibility of their reaching rocky areas is very remote. If however the root encounters rock, this represents a real barrier as usually this rock is very hard and has no cracks.

When the plant rooting is inserted in the alluvial soils of the flat, open plains between the rivers, its roots grow wide and deep, finding loose soil and small, rounded pebbles. However, after descending half a meter, the roots normally come across a white crust which some call "toba", or tufa. This is pure limestone and prevents the roots from passing through due to its hardness, an absence of cracks and the fact that it releases a substance, active limestone, which tends to dry the roots. Therefore the vines do not grow very deep, and are very sensitive to drought and flooding.

Nevertheless, the use of tractors has enabled this crust to be broken during planting and in consequence, the roots reach an undefined depth, finding areas of pebbles and gravel, alternating with loose sandstone.

One may wonder which soils are the best for producing quality wine. It is difficult to give a simple answer, but we understand that the best soil is marl, which covers practically the entire Rioja Alavesa and the municipal districts of Fonzaleche, Sajazarra, Villalba, Briñas, Haro, Briones, Ollauri, Rodezno, Cenicero, Fuenmayor, San Vicente, Abalos, San Asensio and Uruñuela in the Rioja Alta.

However, there are also vineyards on other soils which produce wines of high quality, such as those of Tirgo, Cuzcurrita, Huércanos, Cordovín, Badarán, Ausejo, Tudelilla, Aldeanueva and San Adrián, among many others.

But despite the importance of the soil, there is another, intimately related factor - the climate.

THE CLIMATE

The Sierra Cantabria protects the vineyards of the Rioja Alta and Rioja Alavesa from the cold winds of the North.

The Rioja is defined, from the point of view of climate, as "an arrowhead of Mediterranean light within the mists of the Cantabrican sea". It is an area of northern luminosity within our peninsula. It has, in turn, another singular characteristic: The Rioja, through the Basque Country, which is the area of the Cantabrican region which has the lowest mountains, receives winds from the Atlantic ocean with more ease than other inland areas where they are intercepted by the mountains of the "Picos de Europa" and the Pyrenees. The winds which the vineyards receive from the Atlantic bring with them a breath of quality, much in the same way as in Jerez, Oporto, Bordeaux, the Rhine, etc. Thus, the vineyards of the Rioja represent a delightful blend of Atlantic and Mediterranean climates.

Within the Rioja itself, the climates are extremely varied and a simple observation of the crops gives some idea of this. From Haro to Alfaro vines, almonds, olives and peaches are grown in progressive stages. The specific data is shown in the following chart:

Locality	Annual rainfall	Average temperature	Hours of sunshine
Haro	499 mm	12.7 ºC	1.977
Logroño	390 mm	13.1 ºC	2.150
Alfaro	284 mm	14.4 ºC	2.385

Viticulture combines these pieces of data by means of the "bioclimatic index" which takes active temperatures into consideration, i.e. those of more than 10 ºC, the days of sunshine and rain; all with reference to the 190 days counted annually from bud break to the grape harvest. In this way, the "bioclimatic scale" gives the Rioja Alta a figure of around five, a little more (not quite six) for the Rioja Alavesa and nine for the Rioja Baja. Figures of between four and seven are to be considered optimum for fine table wines. At lower levels, "chacolis" (a slightly acidic white wine made in the Basque Country) are produced and at higher levels, low quality wines.

The clearest way in which climate influences the quality of wine is in the alcohol content. The higher the temperature and level of luminosity, the more sugar the grape will have; therefore the wine will have a higher alcohol level. In this way, and as can be seen on the map below, wines from "Las Conchas de Haro" to Alfaro vary from ten to fifteen degrees of alcohol, although wine producers try to reduce these extremes by blending selected wines.

But fine wines, such as those produced in the Rioja, cannot be valued according to their alcohol content; but according to the colour, palate and aroma, which in some respects is opposite to their alcohol content. Thus, the fine wines which are bottled in the Rioja usually have between eleven and thirteen degrees of alcohol.

The comments we have made regarding climate refer to the specific habitat of the vineyards. Nevertheless, there are annual climatic variations which make the grape harvest very good in some vineyards and deficient in others. The more important of these variations are due to frost, wind and rain.

When we mention frost, we do not refer to the cold in winter, but temperatures of under four degrees which affect the vines during spring and autumn. These cold spells slow down the vegetation process of the vine and cause harvests of unripened, low-quality grapes. When these cold spells occur regularly in May and June, low-quality vintages can be predicted.

We have detected an interesting piece of data: good, high-quality wine harvests are preceded by prevailing northerly and westerly winds during growth and until September. On the other hand, poor-quality vintages are preceded by prevailing winds from the South-East. The beneficial effect of the Atlantic is clear.

Excess rainfall provokes the risk of infection from dangerous diseases of the vine: mildew, and grey rot. In these cases the wines have poor colour.

It is important to understand that Rioja wine is the product of very specific climatic conditions and therefore, for Rioja wine producers, the risk of a sub-standard harvest is ever present. Although Rioja wine reaches a certain quality level every year, only some years does the climate allow an extraordinary or excellent quality appropriate for constituting "Reservas". In other words, wine of sufficient character and structure to enhance quality after many years of ageing.

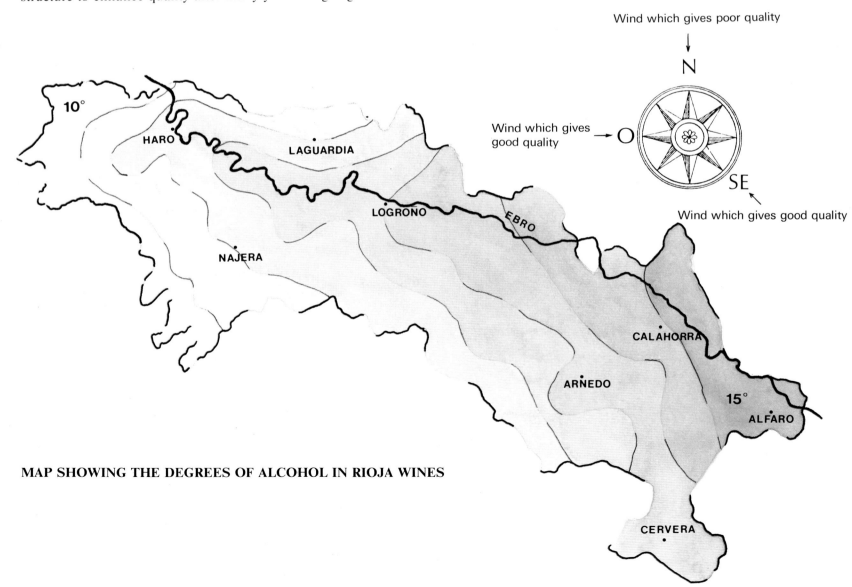

MAP SHOWING THE DEGREES OF ALCOHOL IN RIOJA WINES

THE HUMAN FACTOR

The most recent studies of fossilised plants suggest that vines first appeared in Transcaucasia. Perhaps in those lands "Noah planted the vine" (Genesis IX, 20). Afterwards the presence of vines began to expand to the east and towards the west. Wine flowed during the feasts of Bacchus and Dionysus. The definition of the just measure of this "delightful drink" was used as a prologue to Plato's "Banquet".

The Greeks brought vines to our western coastline. Romans and christianisation extended their plantation inland. This process brought vines to the Rioja, probably with a very different level of intensity to that found in present plantations. Perhaps Rioja Alta was not a wine-producing area? The arrival of Islam with uprootings in dominated lands, may have caused it the planting of vines, for the first time, in northern areas and, of course, in the climatic "corner" of the Rioja Alta. Paradoxically Islam indirectly exercised an optimum viticultural selection from the point of view of modern-day enology; although, of course, this selection was not consolidated. In the Rioja Alta and in more northerly areas, vines invaded "ortos, hereditates, sernas", all types of worked land. This intensification of vine-growing was followed by an attempt to force production with irrigation "... ad rigandun ortos suos, aut vineas, aut hereditates...".

A thousand years ago, the first intentions to produce wine took root in the Rioja. In those days it was the pilgrim road to Santiago that was the motivation; today, it is the European Common Market.

Huet de Lemps defines Rioja wine as the consequence of an "intelligent attitude in an exceptional environment". An environment which is highly favourable for vines and men who are capable of working them with intelligence. All of this is subtle, as Azorín expressed, referring perhaps, when mentioning the word Rioja, both to the environment and man. Subtlety and perspicaciousness which, when based on simple tasks, and insignificant work without intending it, have become very important. As with the sharp marginal note of the anonymous interpreter of the "Glosas Emilianenses" which, based on a rebellious action, has served as the basis, "per excellence", of the Hispanic academic structure. Such was the miracle of San Millán who multiplied unused wine, perhaps to avoid suspicion, without using water as the starting point. As were the Quintano brothers of Labastida, a clergyman and an army officer, who

established the Bordeaux system, replacing the traditional ageing techniques which had been applied to their wines.

At first, Rioja wine producers vatted their grapes whole, which favoured intercellular fermentation. Afterwards they separated the typical qualities of "lágrima", "medio" and "corazón", using the latter, the strongest, for ageing. More than a century ago this tradition was replaced by the Bordeaux method which established a standard volume for ageing casks and the racking method; as well as the custom of destemming to obtain agreable wines.

Such an intelligent attitude to grapes - Rioja wine is not made with feet - gives rise to wines with fine aroma, vivid colour and very important bromatological conditions which allows dense thoughts to flow freely. The faithful transfer to the intellect of such a subtle land.

The reader may wonder about the place occupied in this vision of the Rioja and its wine by men who, having come from so far away, were so important for the Rioja in the last century. We could reply with the popular aphorism that the bull does not really come from where it is born but from where it grazes. But it seems undignified to limit man to quirks of chance and to grazing, or if you wish, only to grazing, although

La Rioja, situated on the Road to Santiago de Compostela, has always been a region open to new cultural and ideological trends.

this might evoke a sense of peace. The destiny of these men, wisely, was to concentrate on the land, on the soil where they found their spiritual coordinates, will and imagination. And - what better course to steer by than wine? An exceptional wine, the most important of agricultural products in time, in space and, of course, the only one with a third dimension - ideas.

GRAPE VARIETIES

Vines produce grapes with a wide range of characteristics. The different groups of vines which produce similar grapes represent a variety. The varieties used for the production of grapes for making wine are known as wine-producing varieties. In general terms, each area grows different varieties, but some are remarkable for the little amount of work they require, others for the fine quality of their wine, or for their colour and aroma. They have become important to the world of wine and practice of enology.

The importance of the variety of vine used to obtain wine is considerable; to the extent that it could be said that modern enology is the study of different varieties of the vine. It is understood that, strictly, each type of grape should receive a specific treatment to obtain a wine of maximum quality.

There are six basic wine-producing varieties in the Rioja:

Reds	TEMPRANILLO	MAZUELO		Whites	VIURA
	GRACIANO	GARNACHA			MALVASIA

There are others which are not so important due to their low proportion in the final blend and due to the fact that they do not have a definitive effect on the quality of the wine.

The distribution of these varieties in La Rioja is irregular. The following chart gives an idea of the intensity of this distribution per area (1995):

Variety	Rioja Alta	Rioja Alavesa	Rioja Baja
TEMPRANILLO	65%	85%	20%
MAZUELO	5%	2%	
RED GARNACHA	8%	3%	72%
GRACIANO	5%	2%	
VIURA	15%	5%	3%
MALVASIA	1%		
OTHER VARIETIES	1%	3%	5%

The amount of vine stocks planted in each municipal district of the Rioja is also variable. Vines are not the only crop and the size of these districts is variable. As examples of districts which have more than four million vines, we can mention Aldeanueva, Alfaro, Ausejo, Autol, Cenicero, San Asensio and Tudelilla. With almost three million vines, Alcanadre, Briones, Elciego, Haro, Labastida, Lapuebla and San Vicente, among others.

In very general terms, two different habitats of vines for producing Rioja wine can be distinguished: the domain or habitat of the Tempranillo in the western area (Rioja Alta and Alavesa) and the dominion or habitat of the red Garnacha in the eastern area (Rioja Baja). This distribution into areas has been developed over the centuries due, basically, to factors of climate. The semi-arid eastern area allows for the easy production of the red Garnacha which is hardier than the Tempranillo; this variety being somewhat delicate. On the other hand, the semi-humid western area, is not favourable for the Garnacha as the cold hinders flowering and produces wines with little colour; but it is very easy to produce grapes of an intense colour with the Tempranillo variety.

We should like to offer lovers of Rioja wines a simple method of identifying the different grape varieties in the vineyards. This method is applicable only to maturing grapes, i.e., as of September 10th. We shall describe the typical bunches. In addition, we insist that the fruit be handled to help distinguish between the different varieties. "By their fruit you shall know them" has a just application in order to discern the difference. The vines live up to our beliefs.

This is the method of differentiation:

White grapes	Yellowish-green grape which when squeezed in one's hand maintains its colour without alteration for one minute	VIURA
	Golden-yellow grape which when squeezed in one's hand changes to darker tones at the end of one minute	MALVASIA
Red grapes	Ash-grey external appearance which when squeezed in one's hand changes colour from a reddish tone to brown after one minute .	GRACIANO
	Reddish-black grape. When squeezed in one's hand it changes colour from red to brown	GARNACHA
	When squeezed in one's hand they maintain their reddish colour for one minute: Intense red	TEMPRANILLO
	Pale red	MAZUELO

TEMPRANILLO

This red variety is considered as being native to the Rioja. It is, perhaps the most highly-esteemed variety.

It gives the red wine of the Rioja its characteristic flavour and has become one of the world's most interesting varieties.

The grape is often very sweet, with low acidity. It provides smooth, velvety wines with an intense colour, appropriate for immediate consumption; also for long-term ageing. Its colour is very stable during ageing and offers very fine characteristic aromas in bottled wines. It is a variety which releases high amounts of glycerine and lactic acid during fermentation; this provides its velvety nature. Nevertheless, due to the low fixed acidity, its processing, and energetic fermentation is difficult, creating problems for the enologist.

It reaches its highest quality in the Cenicero-Elciego-San Vicente triangle.

GRACIANO

This red variety represents an interesting minority in the Rioja; it characterises its wines with a distinctive aroma.

The colouring matter of this grape is intense but with low stability, the red quickly changes to the brown usually associated with old wine.

It seems to reach its highest quality in the Villalba,-Briones-Labastida triangle.

It is, moreover, a grape which provides a must that oxidises easily. For this reason, wines made entirely from Graciano grapes, although being very aromatic, would also have an unstable colour. Before withering, the leaves take on a shade of red and the grapes, although red when fully mature, have an extremely dusty appearance which is very apparent to the touch. This variety is considered as being native to the Rioja.

The forty-five days which precede ripening bring about important variations in this grape. The skin changes from being very hard to very fragile and there is a sharp rise in the sugar content. The must is difficult to clarify.

GARNACHA

A red variety with an intense colour which quickly assumes the brown hues of an aged wine. It often causes sediments in the bottle. It is a variety which "oxidises" easily; if the wine is submitted to a long period of ageing in casks it can become rancid.

Due to tartaric acid, which is plentiful in the grape, it possesses a strong fixed acidity, giving the wine a "hard" taste. They are agreeable wines during the first two years but afterwards they lose quality. They reach their best quality in the Ausejo-Arnedo-San Adrián triangle.

This is a hardy variety, i.e., it does not require great care. Nevertheless, the flowering and fructification is more difficult in cold areas.

The characteristic instability of wines made purely from Garnacha is due to the oxidability or browning of its must when in contact with air. The wines tend to age extremely quickly. This means that the wine improves during ageing until it reaches optimum quality; afterwards it declines quickly becoming cloudy and astringent.

In the area around Labastida, it is blended with Tempranillo, to give a stronger quality to the wines. In the more western part of the Rioja, in Sajazarra, Fonzaleche, etc., the colour matures very badly; however excellent rosés can be produced.

MAZUELO

A red variety characterised by its production of grapes with very little colour. Nevertheless, this colour, although moderate, is very stable throughout long years of ageing. It is, perhaps, the Rioja grape which is responsible for the longest-lasting colour in wine. It does not reach a high degree of alcohol but it does have a strong fixed acidity. These conditions of colour stability and intense fixed acidity, give this variety an important role in the production and ageing of red wines known as "Rioja claret". In the strict sense, these are red wines with a lively colour and a strong fruity aroma.

Although the colour of Mazuelo does not lose its intensity during long periods of ageing, it does vary in tone, from ruby-red to brick-red.

It reaches its highest quality in the Haro-Villalba-Tirgo triangle.

VIURA

The basic variety for Rioja white wines. It provides very pale-coloured fruity wines with a strong fixed acidity. Very appropriate for drinking when young or for ageing in barrels.

Its wine is highly resistant to oxidation.

Red wine produced exclusively with Tempranillo benefits when blended with 15% Viura.

It reaches its highest quality in the Villalba-Tirgo-Cenicero triangle.

When sold as must, this variety is very attractive due its pale colour and freshness.

The area around Haro produces very agreeable, fresh, light wines. In the area pertaining to the province of Alava and the areas of San Asensio, Cenicero and Fuenmayor, if it is fermented at less than 25ºC, it gives a very aromatic, fruity, dense wine, with good body and "extract". On the other hand, when fermented at 30ºC it gives wines which are appropriate for ageing.

It is advisable to bring harvesting forward slightly when half a gram of malic acid remains. Its grapes are also very apt for "cava" sparkling wines.

It is the essence of Rioja white wine.

In the area of Oyón and Lapuebla, within the province of Alava, it is used abundantly as a component for red wines, at a proportion of more than 20%.

MALVASIA

White variety which produces wines with distinctive fruity aromas, and a highly-defined golden colour. During long ageing periods the wine tends to maderise and become cloudy when bottled.

They have a smooth taste, with a low acidity level, and are appropriate for consumption during the first two years.

It reaches its best quality in the Haro-Tirgo-San Asensio triangle.

Wines made entirely from Malvasia are very agreeable during the first year or two, but not so in the following years, due to the changes of colour and appearance.

The must is at first greenish-yellow but it quickly takes on a golden hue. When fermented at under 20ºC it provides maximum aroma. At more than 25ºC these aromas are lost.

It is a delicate grape which is very prone to grey rot.

The wine scarcely has a "green" taste.

In the area around Haro it gives very agreeable fresh, light wines.

The introduction of new frames allowing for tractors, has not altered the density of vines per hectare, although it has modified the surface area dedicated to each vine. Thus, a frequently-used modern frame measures 2.6 m x 1.3 m, and means 2,958 vines per hectare.

During more remote times it seems that the "royal frame" used measured two "varas", i.e., 1.67 x 1.67 m.

It is customary in the Rioja to carry out planting from February 15th and before 20th April. Taking advantage of the Spring rains and humidity, avoiding the droughts and frosts of other seasons.

ROOT SYSTEM OF PLANTED VINES

Free development, according to the soil type,
for vines of 20-30 years of age.

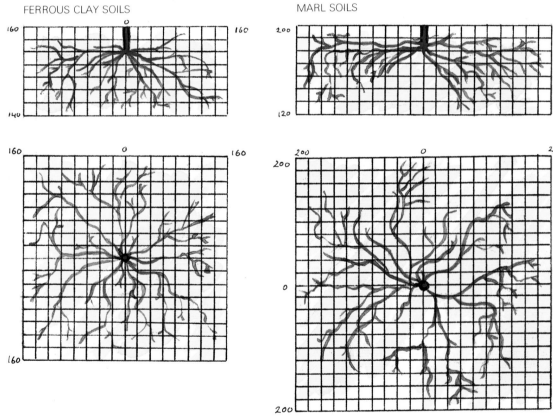

FERROUS CLAY SOILS

MARL SOILS

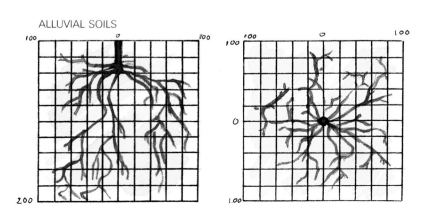

ALLUVIAL SOILS

STOCK AND GRAFT

Grafting is a very delicate operation which requires great care.

After the phylloxera invasion, the roots of local vineyards were seriously damaged and it was necessary to consider reconstruction. Use was made of vines typical in phylloxera prone areas. If this pest came from North America, the solution also came from that country, where vines and disease live together in harmony. The European vines were reconstructed on an American root which was resistant to phylloxera; the upper part being capable of producing European grapes, the grape of the American vine is inappropiate. In this way, almost all existing vineyards have a "foot" or stock of the American vine with a graft of traditional vines from the Rioja.

Another circumstance influences the grafting operation. This involves a chemical reaction of the American vine root. This vine does not stand up as well as the European vine to the so-called active limestone in the soil, which in the Rioja can be plentiful.

Therefore, faced with the phylloxera attack, vinegrowers sought American vine roots resistant to the limestone present in their vineyards. But other factors, in addition to limestone, are taken into consideration when choosing a stock, such as:

Depth of the arable soil
The variety of European vine which is to be grafted
Dryness of the area
The desired production
The salinity of the soil

What happens if the vinegrower does not graft? If the vinegrower plants a vine without grafting, he might do this with European vines which are susceptible to attack by phylloxera; their roots would not resist the attacks of this insect. Its productive life would only reach twenty years. But if he does not graft, we can also suppose he will plant American vines, in which case the vine lives a long time but produces inadequate grapes for wine-making. They will be rejected by the market due to a colour component called "malvina".

The European variety of vine, from which we obtain our wines has the scientific name of Vitis vinifera, while the American vines, from which come the phylloxera-resistant stocks, are of the following species:

Vitis rupestris
Vitis riparia
Vitis labrusca
Vitis berlandieri

From experimental crosses of these American species, numerous stocks have developed. The most common of these, as used in the Rioja, are as follows:

Popular name	Origin of cross	Resistance to active limestone up to
3.309	Riparia x Rupestris	0-11%
Rupestri de Lot	Rupestris variety of Lot	0-14%
99 R	(Richter) Berlandieri x Rupestris de Lot	0-17%
110 R	(Richter) Berlandieri x Rupestris	0-17%
161-49	Ripari x Berlandieri	0-25%
41-B	Chasselas (V. vinifera) x Berlandieri	0-50%

The grafting operation consists of joining recent cuts of the stock and graft. The cut is usually clean and oblique although it can be made with split mesh or with a scion. After a year in the soil, this grafting operation can be carried out where the stock is planted. This is the traditional system in La Rioja. In addition, it is possible to operate with the "taller" or "workshop" graft, this is the joining of the stock and graft in the nursery before planting in the vineyard. In this way a year is gained in the process of preparing the vineyard. Recently, the "pote" or "pot" system has been used, whereby grafts made in nurseries and rooted there are later transplanted to the vineyard with some earth which envelops the roots in a small perforated tub which afterwards decomposes in the soil.

Red and white vines give colour to the fields
of La Rioja.

Roots search for dampness through the rock and can grow many metres length and depth.

ROOTS

The vine gives out a tap-root from seeds, i.e., a main root which descends deeply into the ground and sends out branches at different heights. Nevertheless, according to vine-growing practices, use is not made of the germination of seeds, as the vine reproduces by means of "estacas" or cuttings which are rooted in nurseries and transplanted to the vineyard. In this case, the root develops in stages from the bottom end of the cutting, although, after some years roots also come out of higher parts of the cutting.

The dimensions of the root system of vines, as in the case of other arborescent or shrub-like plants, depend on the characteristics of the soil in which they are planted, on the planting density, on the type of stock, on the characteristics of the variety and the cultivation method (ploughing, working, fertilization, etc.).

The type of soil is highly important for the shape and dimension of the root system of the vine. For a "royal frame" of 2 x 2 metres and a 20-year-old vine, we have found the following dimensions:

SOIL TYPE	MAXIMUM DEPTH (metre)	MAXIMUM EXTENSION (radius in metres)	MAXIMUM ABSORPTION (at depth)
Marl	1.15	1.87	0.45
Ferrous clay	1.29	1.42	0.66
Alluvial soils	1.97	1.87	0.87

The dimensions in alluvial soil refer to soils where the limestone crust has been broken, as is the case with present planting techniques. Formerly, the maximum depth of this soil would only be about 60 centimetres.

The planting density and frame have influence on the development of the root system. When the density is high, i.e., when there are other vines very near, the vine tends to send its roots very deep. On the other hand, when they are widely separated, after some years the roots spread and do not go very deep.

In marl soils, the roots can easily penetrate the cracks in sandstone-limestone and develop in a very irregular way, both in shape and depth. It is interesting to note that there are vines planted in rocks by means of a drill which perforates the soft rock as far as the stratum of loose soil. In this way, the vine seems to grow on the rock, but this only covers the non-absorbent part of the root. Underneath, the roots extend easily.

Root-cutting is carried out during the 2nd year.

45

After some years, vines assume strange shapes.

TRUNK AND MAIN STEMS OR "ARMS"

In the Rioja, vines have a shape similar to a "candelabra". This does not occur naturally but is the consequence of pruning. The vinegrower obtains this shape intentionally during the pruning operation each year. This shape is also known as "goblet" pruning.

Two or three years after grafting and at about 10 cm from the soil, the trunk of the vine divides into three branches. On each branch, two canes are cut back at the base, leaving two buds on each, but year after year and once the three branches have formed, these do not continue to fork. Although two buds are left on each spur, and from these canes shoot each year, the upper one is eliminated and the lowest, two buds away, is pruned in turn. In this way, every year, the trunk which supports three branches, each with two spurs, is left with twelve buds, two on each cane.

Step by step, year after year, the trunk and branches become coriaceous with black, exfoliable bark. The canes which become renewal spurs and afterwards form part of the "arms", change from green to a reddish colour, then ochre, which pales and after two years, becoming greyish and then black or very dark brown.

Up to an age of twenty-five years, the branches grow in the harmonious form of a goblet or cup. Afterwards, and to avoid excessive height, the vinegrower tends to cut back further growth producing, during the course of the next twenty years, spiral or zig-zag shapes, sometimes with a downward tendency. After more than sixty years, the shapes can become picturesque.

In the Rioja Baja there are pruned vines with shorter branches but with a higher common trunk. In the Rioja Alta the branches start at 20-30 cm and the cup shape reaches 50 cm after twenty years. On the other hand, in the Rioja Baja the trunk reaches 40 cm and the branches an extra 10 cm.

Several vegetative forms arise each year in the vine as a whole.

At intervals of 15-25 cm along the canes there are thicker sections which indicate knots. These bring together buds, leaves, tendrils, bunches and internal diaphragm. The arrangement of the trunk and branches according to the wishes of the vinegrower, does not have any definite effect on the quality or quantity of grapes. In the Rioja it has the shape of a goblet as this is the simplest shape to occupy the space available in the vineyard.

As a consequence of modern cultivating methods, without horses, the arrangement of the vines and their shape can be varied to simplify work. This, does not influence the quality of the wine as long as no attempt is made to obtain a higher yield than that permitted by regulations.

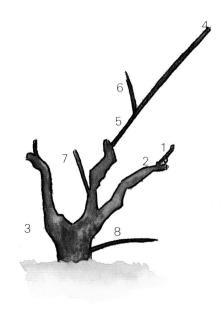

1. Auxillary buds in the axils of the leaves. These are the two buds which are counted for production on each spur.
2. Base buds on spur.
3. Adventitious bud on old wood.
4. Terminal bud at the end of the cane.
5. Shoot on each spur.
6. Lateral shoots. Shoot on each cane.
7. Watersprout. Shoot on old wood.
8. Stock-sucker. Shoot from the lower part of the trunk, from stock wood.

A. Base of the bunch or tendril.
B. Bark.
C. Diaphragm.
D. Pith.
E. Wood.
F. Bud.
G. Leaf. Petiole.

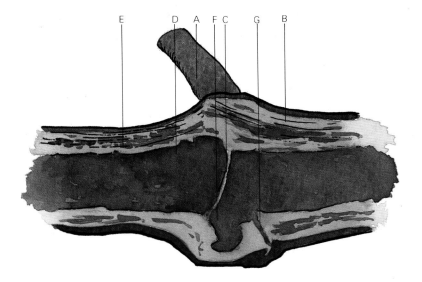

THE PRODUCTIVE PERIOD

Vines can live up to one hundred years. Nevertheless, from the point of view of producing grapes for wine-making, the life of the vine is considered as being shorter. The maximum life for a vine in the Rioja, although defined by age, is the accumulation of factors which exhaust the vine, such as:

a) Repeated diseases.
b) Pruning done in such a way as to increase production.
c) Droughts.
d) Damage caused by machinery.

Lately, in isolated instances, we have found cases of sudden withering of Rioja vines. This occurs in vines during the ripening stage, which, apparently, have healthy roots, trunk and produce a large number of grapes. Suddenly, the green parts of the vine begin to dry up, the leaves fall and the bunches cease to ripen. The following year the vine shows no sign of life.

The productivity of the vine in the Rioja is of great interest to the enologist due, not only to the amount it produces, but to the quality of its grapes.

The enclosed chart has been prepared to show the variations in production of a vine throughout a period of one hundred years. Also for production which ranges from zero to three kilogrammes per vine. The thick broken line represents the strict production for each year and the fine dotted line expresses the tendency of each stage in the life of the vine. These tendencies are as follows:

I   Vine-formation stage. It spans the period from zero to four years. Productivity is negligible.

II   Stage of increasing productivity. It spans the period from five to thirty-five years, with an increasing production per vine from 0.2 Kg to 2.7 Kg.

III Stage of declining productivity from thirty-five to fifty-four years. During this stage, productivity descends from 2.7 Kg to 0.75 Kg.

IV   Final stage. From fifty-four years onwards vines produce a steadily decreasing number of grapes, with levels of under 1 Kg per vine.

Therefore, at its most profitable with regard to quantity, the vine is estimated to be about forty years old. In order to pay off the high costs of planting, attempts are made to shorten the "formation" period of the vine. But if we try to force production (as is shown by the yellow line) we also bring forward the stage of declining production; the period of productivity would only reach thirty years. However, as in so many cases, the conflict is essentially one of quality and quantity. Profitability in terms of quantity occurs during a maximum period of forty years, but better quality is attained after the twentieth year.

Another interesting piece of information is that the Control of Origin of the Rioja admits a maximum production per hectare of 6,500 Kg of grapes for red wines. This means that any vine pruned strictly according to local practices between years 25 and 37 of its productive life, exceeds the official rate set by the Control of Origin.

The pride of the Rioja wineproducer.

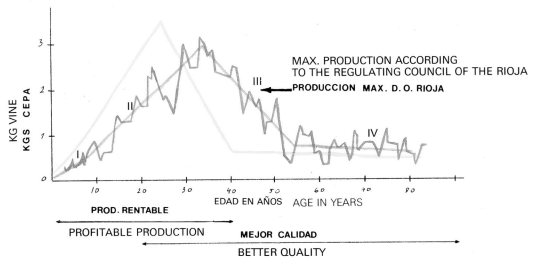

MAX. PRODUCTION ACCORDING TO THE REGULATING COUNCIL OF THE RIOJA
PRODUCCION MAX. D. O. RIOJA

KG VINE / KGS CEPA

EDAD EN AÑOS   AGE IN YEARS

PROD. RENTABLE

PROFITABLE PRODUCTION

MEJOR CALIDAD

BETTER QUALITY

48

Bunch of Graciano grapes

Above the brown line denoting productivity stages, the climatic circumstances of each year allow fluctuations in the quantity of grapes produced by about 40%, both above and below the normal figure.

Sometimes, in order to revitalise vines of more than sixty years old the trunk is cut a short distance above the ground so that the latent buds of the old wood can give rise to a new productive structure. Thus the distance over which the sap has to flow is reduced. One of the causes for exhaustion is the progressive height of the vine trunk with the consequent difficulty for the movement of nutritive liquids.

Soils have a negligible influence on the life of a vine, although it seems that dry soils, marls, far from underground streams can, as a result of droughts, limit the life of a vine.

ANNUAL CULTIVATION

Vines are domesticated plants which would have great difficulty in adapting to the wild. Frequently, vines which are not looked after become diseased, wither and die, even though it would appear natural that, without pruning and cultivation, they would develop into a thick tangle of leaves and canes. An abandoned vine dies despite having soil and sun.

The attentions which vines must receive annually in the Rioja in order to maintain their level of quality production are several and can be grouped into:

Care of the soil.
Care of the plant.
Treatment of possible diseases.

We have already seen that the vegetative cycle of the vine spans the period from April to October. During this time care is necessary, especially during the initial stage from budding to flowering. This period lasts about sixty days (April and May), the vines go through two complex, delicate and energy-absorbing stages: Budding and flowering/fertilisation, both coinciding with the wet period of spring in the Rioja.

For all these reasons, from April 1st until the end of May, greater care must be given than at other times.

The attention given to the soil has the basic aim of maintaining the humidity received by the soil and to prevent rain water from running away. The attention given vines during this period tends to simplify the growth required to produce the canes. In turn, favouring in the development of bunches or the fertilization of flowers and to give the green mass of vines a pleasant appearance.

At the beginning of April it is usual practice to separate the earth that some months before had surrounded the trunk to defend it against winter frosts. This separation of earth creates a space around the trunk which enables rain water to penetrate the area next to it.

About two weeks later, the vine having already sprouted, buds appear on the old wood of the trunk, spoiling the appearance of the vine and consuming energy and water. For this reason, "espergura" or trimming takes place, which many Rioja vinegrowers also call "espervura". In short, it is a "purging" or cleaning of the trunks. Shoots sprouting from the trunk are removed by hand. In addition, other plants will have grown spontaneously among the vines, these are also removed. They disfigure the vineyard and consume the scarce amounts of water. The soil is broken up at the same time to allow for the absorption of the rain. If the soil were not loose and broken up, rain would run off without penetrating into the soil, especially in the case of vineyards planted on hillsides.

At the end of April, canes tend to develop smaller leaves among the main ones, fruit of the secondary buds on these canes. This would lead to an excessive ramification of the vine. Therefore these shoots are removed by hand in an operation which is called "desniete" or the removal of lateral shoots. Due to this operation, the development of excessive foliation is avoided and energy is retained in the lower part of the canes where the clusters of grapes are formed. At the same time the weeds are again removed so that the soil, the upper layers of which are loose, can withstand the loss of moisture due to evaporation in the summer heat. As of that moment the development of the canes does not allow working between the vines, although this is facilitated by the rows and lanes of modern vineyards.

At the end of May "despunte" or "tipping" is carried out consisting of cutting back the lengthwise growth of the canes and retaining the energy involved to favour flowering. Tipping may be repeated after flowering for the benefit of the clusters of grapes: cutting back leaves at the same time so that the grapes can swell. Nevertheless, in vineyards which are unprotected from the wind, tipping, or the cutting back of about 40 cm from the end of the cane, is also necessary in order to remove a surface on which the wind can exert a considerable force, breaking them off at the base. This part is still tender and weak but in June hardens and changes into wood.

Treatment to prevent the possibility of disease can be made at the same time as this work is carried out.

← "Viña Alberdi" estate in Rodenzo (22 Ha.).

First week of April.
EARTHING UP

Middle of April
TRIMMING AND HARROWING

End of April
REMOVAL OF LATERAL
SHOOTS AND HARROWING

RIPENING

Ripening is the culmination of the fruit on the vine. It begins in August, after the "envero" or "veraison" and involves a series of gradual processes which start with the green grape and finish with the ripe grape; which is picked and goes on to the fermentation process.

It is an over simplification to say that when the grape ripens its sugar content increases. This is clear, but is only one aspect of the many which can be observed.

We must distinguish between physical aspects such as the variation in the size of the grape, variation in its hardness and weight, and chemical aspects such as the increase in sugar, the loss of acidity and oxidability.

We offer the reader three charts which, with eight curves, express the essential points of this process. In all these charts, the horizontal axis represents time from three points of view:

− DAYS. As the number of days which elapse from budding.

− Bioclimatic index or the accumulation of solar energy for ripening.

− CALENDAR MONTHS.

The vertical axes of each chart express a different aspect, namely:

No. 1. The total acidity of the grapes per kilogramme of pressed grapes. We can see that after September, this declines rapidly.

No. 2. Expresses another concept of acidity called pH, which is the true acid taste. This value rises in September and shows that the acid taste diminishes.

No. 3. Grapes contain many different acids. Tartaric acid is the typical acid in grapes, but there is also malic acid, which is typical in apples, and even some citric acid, normally associated with oranges. All these occur naturally. The later we leave the grape-harvest the lower the amount of acidity there will be in the grape. If we bring the grape-harvest forward, the wine will taste strongly of malic acid. It will be a so-called "green" wine.

No. 4. This represents the oxidability of the must. The more mature the grape, the more oxidable the must will be. On oxidising, or on contact with air, white grapes take on strong golden tones or brown in the case of red grapes. The riper the grape, the more easily this occurs.

No. 5. This curve represents the probable alcohol content. The alcohol which the wine will have depends on the sugar content of the grape. We can see that this is the most obvious aspect of the ripening process; from about four degrees at the beginning of September, up to thirteen, at the end of October.

No. 6. At the same time as these chemical changes occur, the grape also varies. Should we wish to perforate a grape with a needle we would need about two hundred grammes of force in August, and perhaps, only ten grammes in October.

No. 7. The size also increases from nine millimetres in diameter in August, to sixteen in October.

No. 8. This represents the increase in weight of the berry or grape. After September, the weight does not rise, but as the diameter continues to increase, it can be deduced that the density or the richness of the sugar increases, as can be seen in the graph of probable degrees.

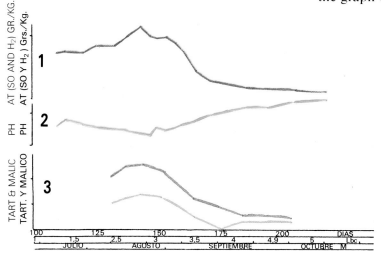

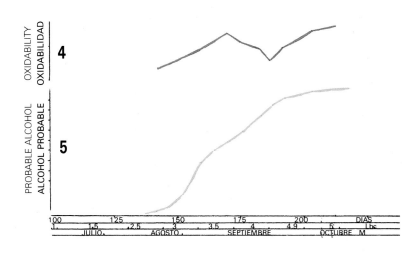

Vineyard in San Vicente de la Sonsierra

To sum up, for Rioja wine, the ripening of the grapes involves a series of complex changes in the grape from August to September.

Increases: The sugar content increases in the grape, which afterwards will produce the alcohol. The weight and size of the grape increases as well as the oxidability of the must, not forgetting the colour of the grape skin in the case of red varieties.

Decreases: The acid content goes down, and with it the acid taste as well as the hardness of the skin.

We can understand that if we bring the grape harvest forward two weeks, we will obtain a wine with a lower alcohol content, less colour and more acidity than in the case of a late harvest.

The data on these charts has been taken from the Rioja Alta (Cenicero, Briones, Haro and Villalba). The typical date of the grape-harvest of this area is the festival of Santa Teresa. A date which indicates, year after year, an acceptable level of ripeness for the great wines of the Rioja.

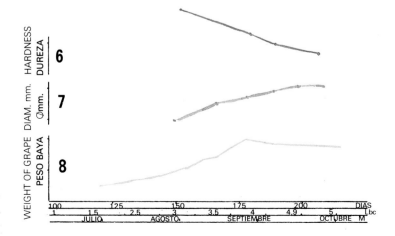

Grape harvest on the "Viña Ardanza I" estate. (65 Ha.) in Cenicero.

THE HARVEST - QUALITY AND QUANTITY

The harvest is the traditional operation of collecting grapes and is, partly representative in itself of a season of the year: the Autumn.

Rioja wineproducers usually collect their grapes during the first fortnight of October. However, year in, year out, the question arises-when to harvest? The weather during the year may have been favourable and the harvest can be brought forward, or unfavourable and make a late harvest advisable. During that fortnight, any delay means collecting the grapes at a more ripened stage than harvesting at the beginning of October.

The bodegas decide when to harvest their vineyards after analysing their grapes by means of a density meter reading of the must or by means of a refractometer. This indicates that they will produce a wine with a certain degree of alcohol.

Modest wineproducers depend on old fashioned methods. They know that when they squeeze the grape between their fingers and it produces a sticky sensation, the wine might reach twelve degrees. They also know that when the stem begins to turn brown there is no beneficial circulation between root and leaf. On the other hand, some years, the leaves wither early and fall, or turn yellow or brown. The vine grower knows in this case that further ripening is not desirable and it is advisable to harvest.

In general terms, the harvest depends on weather conditions in Autumn. In the Rioja, as in many inland areas, it rains during two periods of the year, in Spring and in Autumn. The rains of Autumn do not benefit the grapes if they occur after the beginning of the month of October. They can even prove to be prejudicial, softening the skin of the grape and favouring the growth of moulds, called Botrytis. This deteriorates the film to the extent that red musts become brown and whites musts excessively golden or brown, too. In these cases, after the rainy season has commenced, it is advisable to start harvesting immediately.

Typically, small wineproducers take advantage of weekend visits from their relatives for this purpose.

Although there is talk of mechanical harvesting in the Rioja, the grape picking is still done by hand and labour costs are fixed at a tenth of the selling price of the grapes.

The harvesting operation is carried out by manual cutting with a curved knife called "corquete". The wineproducer places his left hand under the bunch and with the other moves the "corquete" upwards against the base of the stem. The bunch falls gently into his hand and he transfers it to the collection basket, which are shaped like a truncated cone and have an approximate capacity of 20 Kg. They are open-weave, made from intertwined chestnut fibres or, in some cases, from wicker. However, in the Rioja, chestnut fibres are more typical. Recently, rubber baskets have appeared of the

Wooden tub, basket and pruning knives on the old scales used for weighing harvested grapes.

White grapes are harvested separately from red.

Different aspects of grape harvesting on the "Viña Ardanza I" estate (65 Ha.) in Cenicero.

same shape and capacity. Their maximum diameter is usually 55 cm with a width of 45 cm and a depth of 40 cm. They have two handles.

Once full of grapes, the baskets are carried to the place where the "comportas" or tubs (wooden containers with a 100-Kg capacity) are located. These tubs are in turn loaded onto mules or donkeys, carts or trailers. Today, loading and transport is done by trailers which can hold up to twenty tubs. Horses can carry two, one on each side, like saddlebags, and carts can carry four or six.

"Comportas", or tubs, are shaped like truncated cones, open at the top with a diameter of 60 cm, 1.2 m in height and a base of 40 cm. in diameter. They are made from poplar or chestnut wood with 24 side pieces or "staves". The top has a thickness of 2 cm and the bottom, 4 cm, to withstand the friction of movement on the ground, due to turning and being supported on a single point when tilted by workers. The staves are fastened by four to six lateral metal hoops. They are of a truncated cone shape so that, when empty, they can be piled one inside the other. When full, due to the inclined angle of the side wall, the lower bunches are prevented from being crushed by those on top.

The first harvesting operation, one week before the grape picking, is to soak the tubs in water.

During the harvest these tubs, when they arrive at the bodega, are emptied into the tank or grape mill by being tilted on the edge of the tank, which, many years ago, was a window at the top of the bodega of the wineproducer.

Today, grapes are also carried in tractor-driven trailers, lined with a watertight canvas cover.

The time which elapses from the moment the bunch is cut to their arrival at the bodega has a very important effect on the quality of the wine. The shorter the time, the more probable it is that the wine will be of high quality. Harvested grapes which are kept in baskets for one day cause mould which can be tasted in the finished wine.

If the grapes are kept for one day in the tubs or canvases, the must and resulting wine develops a vinegary taste. The wineproducer realises a need for rapid transport, just as the traditional practice of preventing the grapes from being crushed in the tubs limited the to load to 100 Kg.

Today, there are harvesting machines, which collect the grapes by shaking vines pruned by the espalier method (wires placed in a single line with guided canes). This system is not used in the Rioja.

Grape harvesters must be extremely careful in the selection and handling of bunches.

"Goblot" pruning.

PRUNING

In previous chapters we said that vines are delicate plants. Without attention, they degenerate, taking on a wild look and their production declines.

Pruning is an annual cutting operation; the wood is cut back to avoid the formation of dense foliage, to regulate production, to give consistency to the vine and to facilitate work on the soil.

Distinction can be made between "green" and "dry" pruning. The former is carried out in November or December, also in March, and the latter is done in January or February.

Generally, pruning time in the Rioja is in the middle of the winter, i.e., this involves "dry" or winter pruning. In the higher part of the Rioja Alavesa and Rioja Alta, which are prone to spring frosts, causing a disastrous effect on the quality of the wine, "green" pruning is carried out. After the grape harvest, the leaves wither and fall. The sap of the leaves and canes descends slowly towards the trunk to accumulate and form the winter reserves which will give strength to the new shoots. If we prune when the sap is descending, when the cane is still a little green, part of the sap is removed, i.e., the reserves which would accumulate in winter in the trunk are diminished and the spring shoots would have little strength. However the frosts might cause less damage as the sprouting of buds and leaves would be delayed. If we prune in the middle of the winter, when the sap reserves have already descended to the trunk, it will bring about strong budding; the possible late frosts may damage tender parts of the vine. Therefore, "green" pruning, i.e., with sap in movement, delays budding and protects the vine against Spring or late Winter frosts, but "dry" pruning, in mid-winter does not defend the plant against this risk.

But if pruning is left until late in March, when the vine has bled, generally the vineyard appears overgrown and makes this job difficult. In these cases "pre-pruning", or limited pruning is done, consisting of trimming the canes in December, and carrying out full pruning in March.

Rioja vines have a "goblet" shape, i.e., three ascending stems or "arms". Two "spurs" are left on each branch and two buds on each spur. In this way, the total number of buds per vine is twelve. If we consider that afterwards one cane sprouts

Pruning of a young vine and an old vine.

"Quarante" pruning.

67

Espalier pruning is gaining ground in the Rioja.

from each bud and that each cane bears two clusters of grapes, we can deduce that each vine produces twenty-four bunches. But these theoretical equations are optimistic as there are numerous factors which reduce this amount, such as:

a) Sometimes deficiencies prevent the formation of three branches per vine.
b) Spring frosts sometimes damage the buds.
c) Flowering and fertilisation are not always the same, therefore the "cuajado", or "setting" of the cluster, is different each year, with more or less grapes.
d) Blights and diseases can reduce or obliterate the growth of the clusters.
e) The ripening conditions can increase or decrease the sugar inside the grape, producing clusters with different densities, therefore varying the weight attained the grape-harvest.

In this way we can understand that from twenty-four theoretical bunches, a much lower average, of variable weight, can be gathered per vine.

This type of pruning of twelve buds is typical in the Rioja but in some cases we can observe unorthodox methods which try to leave more than twelve buds to produce more bunches. This is what is called "long pruning". It is somewhat fraudulent and is forbidden by the Control of Origin Regulating Council of the Rioja. In the regulations they specify the pruning of twelve buds, and limit the final weight of grapes produced per hectare to 6.500 Kg of red grapes and 9.000 Kg of white grapes.

Pruning in mist favours cutting ("Viña Ardanza II" estate, 31 Ha. in Fuenmayor).

The espalier method allows bunches to receive
more light during the vegetative cycle.

Is quantity the opposite of quality? Yes. When the vinegrower decides to obtain more grapes with "long pruning", the wine made is of inferior quality to that attained with authorised pruning methods.

Nevertheless, nature may replace these unauthorised methods; some years the weather conditions are so favourable that the amount of grapes obtained per hectare are extremely high and the quality of the wine is excellent. This was the case in 1964, 1970, 1981, 1985 and 1989.

"Two-bud" pruning on goblet-shaped vines is carried out by cutting the previous cane slightly above the two lower buds. Each year these buds are usually left on the lower cane. In this way the vine ascends in a gentle "V-shaped" zig-zag, but in the case of young vines the tendency is to leave the buds on the higher cane. In the case of very old vines, on the lowest canes, which are usually canes from the previous lower bud.

It has been seen that in western areas of the Rioja, grapes receive sufficient nutrients from the soil and products made in the leaves during vegetation; but bunches do not always receive optimum levels of illumination, being in the shade of twigs and leaves. Such lack of light might bring about low colour levels in cold years. To permit bunches to receive more light, pruning is sometimes made along wires, whereby twigs change from a vertical to a horizontal position. They are fastened in this position and exposed to light from the sides and above.

In this case plantations are also made taking into consideration the width and orientation of the passageways, to gain maximum benefit from sunlight. On flat land, the advisable orientation for rows of vines is North-Northwest to South-Southeast.

Within prescribed production limits, this system of training vines can improve the quality of the grapes.

This system is also called "Quarante" pruning.

"Quarante" pruning on the "Viña Arana" estate (36 Ha.), in Rodenzo.

PESTS AND DISEASES

"Coulure" or non-setting of the fruit.

The vine is a plant which is sensitive to several pathogenic diseases. We could say that the finer the variety of grape, the bigger the risk to the vine and clusters of grapes.To a certain extent, this is easy to understand as fine wines come from grapes with very subtle and delicate skins and are, therefore, soft and fragile. In varieties of grapes with hard, herbaceous skins, maceration produces wines which are not very fine but the hardness of the skin protects the grape from external attacks.

In addition to being susceptible to attack by different bacteria, fungi and insects, different eras have had an important influence. The second half of the last century was noteworthy for two new diseases which settled in European vineyards: Oidium and Phylloxera.

Recently (during the last decade) diseases have appeared in the vineyards of the Rioja which, although not devastating, are new in the sense that they are of recent appearance and their incidence is important; namely, Virosis and the Acari.

From viruses to butterflies of the vine (from the pyralid caterpillar) there is an enormous variation in size. The butterfly of the pyralid caterpillar is, at least, a million times bigger than the viruses which exist in some vineyards. This is general in all vinegrowing areas and the situation in the Rioja shows variations in accordance with its microclimates and varieties.

To describe the most typical diseases which affect the vineyards of the Rioja, we shall start with the smallest, the viruses, which have little importance but are of scientific interest. It is believed that they do not only affect the quality of the wine but also the productivity of the vine.

Their size is several thousandths of a millimetre and their presence can be diagnosed by low grape yields, changes (in some cases) in the colour of the leaves and by the length of the canes or production of double canes. The Rioja vinegrower is not disturbed by the presence of these viruses with respect to the quality of his grapes, but the effects they have on yield are indeed important. We do not know how long these viruses have existed in the vineyards of the Rioja. We only know that their presence has just been noticed. New plantations of vines tend to be made with guarantees of absence of these viruses.

The next largest pest is a bacteria, one thousandth of a millimetre in size, which produces necrosis or the death of some tissues of the vine, delaying budding, producing black spots in the wood or in the medulla of the cane, even on its outer part, and by giving very small clusters of grapes. This is not an old disease. Its occurrence is not important but we have mentioned it as a rare and interesting case; there are very few bacteria which attack vines. This disease is easily overcome and eradicated by disinfecting the shears and cuts when pruning the vine. It is a disease which attacks the red Garnacha of the Rioja which, in general terms, is a very resistant variety to other diseases.

Larger in size than bacteria, there are moulds and fungi which attack the vine and are known in the vinegrowing world as "Cryptogams". We name the most important diseases: Oidium and Mildew. The size of these fungi is variable and difficult to describe with precision. They range from a few thousanths of a millimetre in spores to a tenth of a millimetre in filaments.

Oidium is a new disease in Europe and has existed here only since the middle of the last Century. It comes from North America and its effect was felt intensely in the Rioja at the end of the 19th Century. The risk of infection has been constant since then but the disease is easily contained by spraying sulphur powder on the leaves and clusters. The powder reacts with the sun's heat producing sulphurous vapors which kill the fungi growing on the outer surface of the leaves and clusters. Should the fungi not be destroyed, the effects would be disastrous. It attacks the leaves producing granulation and greyish pilosity on the bunches. Vinegrowers call this "cenicilla" or "powdery mildew"; it cracks the skin of the grape, preventing ripening.

Another very important cryptogamous disease is Mildew. Its importance derives from the penetration of the delicate interior of the vine, growing inside, and thus remaining highly resistant to treatment.

Vinegrowers combat this disease with care by using copper sulphate compounds. The important question is when to treat. This disease is a constant risk and occurs when there is a high level of humidity and heat. Sometimes, sporadically, as in 1972, it causes extreme damage and can destroy entire areas of vineyards. Not only do the green parts in the vine die but the trunk also becomes contaminated. Thus, in 1972, due to the rapid invasion of mildew during the month of June, thousands of hectares of vines were destroyed in Spain.

Botrytis.

MILDEW FUNGUS

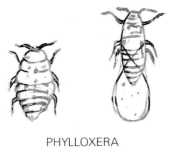

PHYLLOXERA

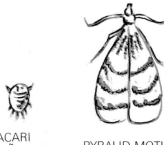

ACARI
"ARAÑUELA"

PYRALID MOTH

.Botrytis

The vineyards of the Rioja, due to their semi-humid nature, are prone to mildew, but the vinegrower has sufficient knowledge and means to deal with it. Mildew attacks the leaves, first producing an oily patch and later destroying it completely. The same thing happens to the bunch of grapes.

Moulds can also attack bunches during the ripening period and during the harvest. This occurs with the Botrytis mould, which grows on soft grapes destroying the bunch and producing musts with deficient colouring and which are highly oxidable. The resulting wines have un unstable colour.

Acari are enemies of the vine and have appeared in the Rioja within the last ten years. The climatic irregularities of this period have produced cold Springs with hesitant budding allowing these acari, red spider, yellow spider and acariosis, to proliferate easily, devouring tender buds and incipient leaves during May. At first, at the beginning of the seventies, their impact was considerable. In the Rioja we were afraid of an escalation of damage due to acari. Despite everything, little by little the Rioja vinegrower, by means of treatment of pruned wood during the winter, has been able to control this pest. Today, it does not represent a danger, although the risk still exists.

The largest of the pests which attack vines are insects.

Several types of insect attack the vineyards and there are few variations between the different vine-growing areas with respect to the importance of these aggressors.

Phylloxera is extremely important. This has affected, devastated and left its mark on all the vineyards of Europe.

As in the case of Oidium, it came from North America. Both invasions first affected Britain and then crossed the Channel to the Continent. Phylloxera reached

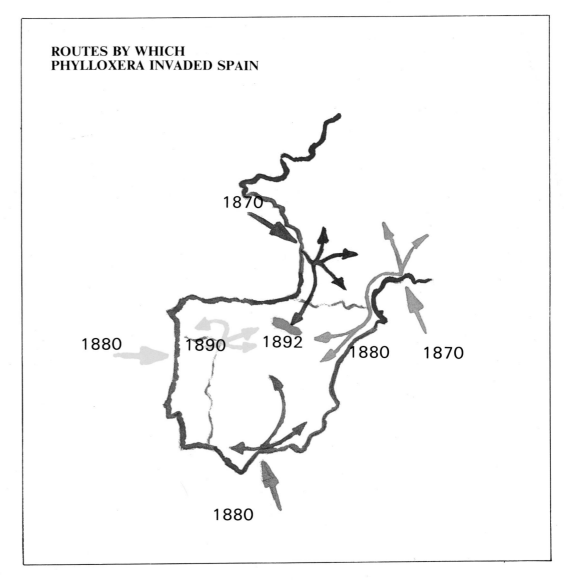

ROUTES BY WHICH PHYLLOXERA INVADED SPAIN

1870

1880   1890   1892   1880   1870

1880

Spanish vineyards by sea. Through Oporto and Málaga in 1880 it began to penetrate the peninsula. However it had already arrived by sea in Bordeaux and the South of France: from there it also extended to the Rioja and Cataluña. The first outbreak in the Rioja was in 1899 in the vineyards of Sajazarra, in the Rioja Alta. It was detected by technicians of the Enological Laboratory of Haro.

Vinegrowers took rapid corrective action by means of American vine stocks which are resistant to phylloxera. Rioja varieties of European vines were grafted on these rootstocks.

Phylloxera has two living forms: one which attacks the roots, piercing them, creating knots causing them to lose vitality; the other, an aerial form, with wings, which pierces the leaves, producing galls or bumps, causing the green parts to disappear if the attack is intense. This plant louse represented the most disastrous invasion of vineyards and is latent in all existing vineyards in the world. The only means of combating it is the creation of plants with American vine roots which withstand the root-attacking type and an upper European part of the vine which provides quality grapes and resists the winged version of phylloxera more than American vines.

Another important insect which offers a possible threat to Rioja vines is the vine pyralid caterpillar. In Spring their larvae appear among the roughness in the bark of the trunk and devour tender shoots, even incipient clusters of grapes, and then change into chrysalises, from which butterflies emerge. This insect is easy to control.

Pests and diseases affect Rioja wine both in quality and quantity. The first effect of a disease in the Rioja is to reduce production. A more intense attack can also delay ripening, producing wines with a "green" taste, little colour and a low alcohol level, therefore not appropriate for long ageing, always desirable in Rioja wines.

These are the general effects, but the attacks to which vines are submitted to during the ripening period, such as Botrytis moulds, can reduce the yield, concentrate the sugar, produce less wine but with a higher alcohol content. There is, however, the inconvenience of colour alteration. Every year, technicians have to face the dilemma of the harvest, namely, to pick early without Botrytis and with little sugar, or later, when the grapes have more sugar but Some Botrytis mould. The choice is simple, harvest late and try to treat Botrytis in the bodega.

FERMENTATION

On the way back to the bodega at the end of the day.

Weighing and sample-taking.

TYPICAL VATTING METHODS

Faced with a glass of red Rioja and others of rosé and white we might think simply that these come from red grapes, from a mixture of red and white grapes or white grapes, respectively. Winemaking is not so simple, and is certainly not so in the Rioja.

The colour of the wines depends both on the colour contributed by the grape and the system of vatting. Vatting is the placing of grapes in containers (between five to fifty thousand kilogrammes) for fermenting.

The wineproducer cuts the bunches of grapes from the vine. Each of these units, or clusters, is made up of the stem, or skeleton of the bunch, and the grapes which adhere to it. Each grape consists of three parts:

1) A film or skin which is colourless in white varieties but for the reds it's the origin of their colour.
2) Colourless pulp or sugared mass. Also colourless for red Rioja varieties.
3) Seeds or pips.

Of these there are two parts which are practically inert, or mostly negative for wine. These are the stems and pips. Based on these notions we can understand the vatting of Rioja grapes and the wines which derive from them.

"Typical vatting": The whole cluster of grapes is thrown into the vat. The pulp ferments with the skins, stems and pips producing red wine, basically from red grapes.

"Classical" vatting. The stems are removed. The pulp, skins and pips are transferred to the vats. Sometimes, the grape is scarcely damaged, only the stem is removed. This is known as destemming. On other occasions, in addition to removing the stem, the grape is crushed. This method is used for red wines only.

"Vatting for rosés". The stems are removed, the grapes are pressed and the pulp, skin and pips are left together for a few hours so that they give some colour to the liquid. Afterwards, the skins and pips are removed and the pale-coloured must ferments. Rosés can be made with a red grape or a mixture of red and white grapes. In this case the contact with the skins is adjusted in accordance with the state of ripeness in order to obtain the desired colour.

"Vatting for white wines": The stems are removed. At a later stage the skins and seeds are also removed. In the Rioja this method is only used for white grapes.

Now we will describe the "typical" vatting method, a tradition which dates back many centuries in the Rioja. This is the artisanal vatting method and no doubt the most primitive.

It consists of throwing whole bunches into the "lagos" or stone vats, they are open containers of stone, cement or oak with a capacity of one or two thousand "cántaras" (from 23,000 to 46,000 Kg). In these containers, the accumulated grapes undergo fermentation.

The process applied in a Rioja bodega can be briefly described with a cross section chart of one of its installations.

Now we shall see what happens in the stone vats. The accumulated grapes fill 80% of the volume of the vat. At the end of five days the mass of grape-clusters begins to heat up to 8 degrees above the initial temperature. After another five days the wineproducer can observe that the level of grapes begins to fall and that foam rises

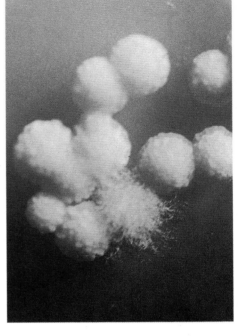

Sowing yeasts in the laboratory.

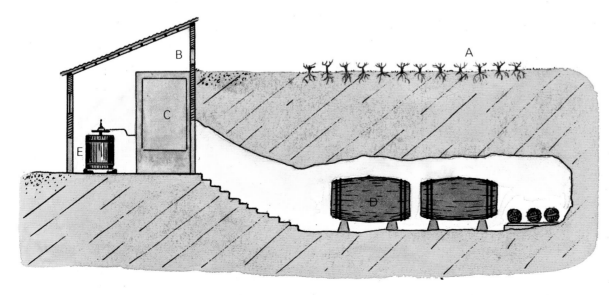

A) Vineyard which is usually near the bodega.
B) The tubs are carried to the bodega from the vineyard and the clusters of grapes are loaded through a window.
C) The grapes fall from the window into the "lago" or stone vat. There, they undergo fermentation.
D) From the stone vat the must-wine goes on to vats for the second fermentation.
E) From the stone vat, solid parts go on to the press and press-wine and pomace are obtained.

from the corners of the vat. This is the moment for devatting or drawing off. To do this, a tap or "canilla" is opened and the first wine called "lágrima" or "tear" flows out. It is the weakest in terms of alcohol content and colour and also has the highest acidity. Once this wine has been drained out, the wineproducer enters the vat, turning over the grapes, at first gently and then stirring with a pitchfork, while another wine flows, the "medio" or "corazón"; it has an intense, smooth colour and a higher alcohol content. This is the best quality wine. The wineproducer continues turning over the grapes until the skins are completely dry. This solid residue is removed through the lower door and then goes on to the press where any remaining moisture is squeezed out.

These wines removed from the stone vats still contain sugar and continue to ferment in underground oak casks.

It is said that every 21,000 to 23,000 Kg of grapes, according to the juiciness of the harvested grapes, produces one thousand "cántaras" (3,500 gallons) of wine. Each Rioja "cántara" contains 16 litres. So from every 22,000 Kg of grapes, an average of 16,000 litres of wine are obtained, which break down into:

"Lágrima"	5,000 litres
"Corazón"	9,000 litres
"Turning" or "Repisado"	1,500 litres
"Press"	500 litres

Fermentation of whole bunches is not current in Spain. It is known that a similar method is applied in the Rhône valley of France. It is a very curious process which scientifically is called intracellular fermentation. In our daily life we have been able to observe that when fruit is kept for more than a day in a closed plastic bag for example, this fruit goes bad: it becomes soft, looses its sweetness and produces something sour. It is a general phenomenon affecting sugared products which, in a closed atmosphere, become saturated with CO_2 from the atmosphere. Each cell of the fruit decomposes and produces carbon dioxide and alcohol. Wineproducers from the Rioja Alavesa and many others from the Rioja Alta and Tudelilla have used this process for centuries.

After five days the stone vat has an atmosphere full of carbon dioxide. The grapes swell due to internal fermentation until, some days later, they split and their pulp, which at first was pale and sweet, becomes fluid, coloured and with a high alcohol content.

The phenomena which occur in each grape are numerous. The most important can be summed up as follows:

I. The sugar of the grape changes into alcohol and carbon dioxide.

II. The colour from the skin begins to move towards the centre of the grape, colouring the pulp.

III. The malic acid, which is responsible for the greenness of the grape, disappears, and changes into another acid: lactic acid. It is curious that within the grape there is (naturally) malic acid which apples contain. This changes into lactic acid, associated with sour milk. For this reason, some good wines of the Rioja have an aroma which reminds one of cheese.

Within the vat, fermentation is not total, as only about eight degrees of alcohol are produced. Afterwards, on drawing off the "lágrima", "corazón", "repisado" and "press" fermentation continues in tubs but this time with the help of yeast, as in the case of normal fermentation.

DAY 1
The recently filled vat contains dry grapes with a few litres of must at the bottom.

DAY 5
The grape has swollen and increased in volume in the vat. At the bottom, there a few thousand litres of must.

DAY 10
The mass of wet grapes drops a little and foam rises at the edges. The liquid which has come out of the grapes now amounts to about 5,000 litres.

DAY 12
After the "lágrima" and "corazón" have been drawn off, the winemaker treads on the skins and flattens them. Afterwards, the door of the vat is opened and the "pasta" is removed.

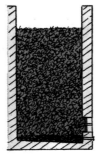

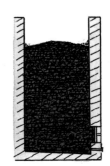

 Recently vatted grape

 After five days it appears swollen

 After ten days it breaks open

 Recently vatted grape (cross section)

 After five days CO_2 bubbles appear. The colour transfers to the pulp (cross section)

 After ten days there is a great deal of CO_2 and the skin breaks. The colour has transferred to the pulp (cross section)

Sample taking is the first quality control which is made with the grapes when they enter the bodega.

Grape reception hopper.

"CLASSICAL" VATTING

At the end of the 18th Century, the inhabitants of the Rioja asked themselves what possibilities there were for exporting their wines. They realised that their wines often suffered from a taste given by the stem. To avoid this, they decided to vat the grapes without stems. The person responsible for this was called Quintano. He lived in Labastida, and applied the Bordeaux methods. We call this the "classical" system, imported from Bordeaux and consisting of vatting the grapes without stems. Although this system is not originally from the Rioja it is the system which, for centuries, has given our wines the great prestige which they enjoy today.

When the harvested grapes arrive at the bodega, they are dropped into a de-stemming machine. Depending on the wishes of the enologist, he can separate the stem only, respecting the structure of the grape, although it becomes somewhat injured. Or, he can operate more violently, remove the stem and crush the grape completely.

The grapes, now without stems, are pumped into the fermentation vats. These usually have a capacity of 25,000 litres and are filled with only 20,000 litres. They are cone-shaped oak vats, or cement or stainless-steel containers.

The grapes, when pumped into the vat, are a homogeneous mass of skin and liquid. After 24 hours, the skin concentrates in the upper part of the container and forms the "sombrero" or "hat". The liquid stays at the bottom. There are an estimated 4,000 litres of "sombrero" and 16,000 litres of liquid. When four days have passed, the yeast which at first adheres to the grapes, multiplies and ferments, i.e., converts the sugar into alcohol, raising the temperature by some 15° C. The presence of CO_2 pushes the "sombrero" upwards. As of the tenth day, fermentation slows down and the "sombrero" sinks slowly into the liquid.

Among the numerous phenomena associated with the fermentation of picked or pressed grapes the following are the most important:

1. The formation of alcohol by the total transformation of the sugar in the fermentation vat.
2. The transfer of the colour from the skins to the liquid. At the same time alcohol is produced and the heat from the fermentation is accumulated.

It is very interesting to observe that this would occur with the fermentation of the whole grape but there is a difference. When the pressed grape ferments, the acid pertaining to the greenness is not destroyed. The wines are richer in acidity.

The enologist must know the fermentation process within each vat once this commences. He must know the quality and if the process is normal or unusual. To do this he carries out three actions. The first of these is to apply CO_2 moderately as an antiseptic guaranteeing the cleaning action of the yeasts: another two controlling actions by means of the assessment of density and temperature.

Due to the sugar the grapes have a high density. When wine is made, as the sugar is transformed, their density decreases. Water has a density of 1.000. Rioja must usually has 1.1 and Rioja wine 0.99. Density control, therefore, varies every day of fermentation from 1.1 to 0.99 and is carried out by using density gauges. The refractometer, which is very useful for measuring the richness of the musts, cannot be used after fermentation begins. The enologist, by means of a density gauge, also knows when fermentation stops. This could be dangerous if there is still some sugar to be transformed.

The screw spindle transfers the grapes to the destemmer.

FERMENTATION CHART

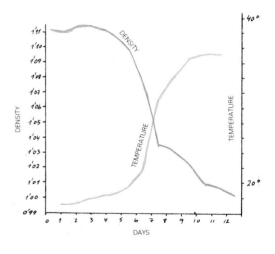

1. Destemmer-squeezer.
2. Stem remover.
3. Pump.
4. Fermentation "cone" (external).
5. "Cone" filled with recently harvested grapes.
6. "Cone" six days after vatting.
7. "Cone" with completely fermented grapes after 12 days.

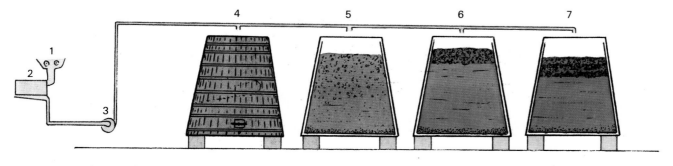

83

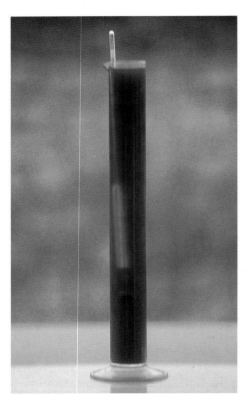

Density gauge

Likewise, the temperature is controlled by means of simple "maximum" thermometers, tied to the end of a pole in order to insert them into the mass during fermentation. The danger of high temperature is great. Let us remember that yeast lives at between 20 and 32 º C. If fermentation accumulates heat up to 35º C, the yeast gives way to bacteria. The ideal temperature for the bacteria is 38º C. They may spoil the wines, making them taste vinegary.

In order to monitor the evolution of the fermentation, the enologist loads data onto fermentation charts. They are prepared with densities and temperatures based on the number of days the grapes have been in the vats.

By means of these charts, the enologist knows the specific values at each moment and their tendencies.

Wines obtained by fermentation of the de-stemmed red grape are more acid than those attained by vatting whole grapes. In turn, those obtained from pressed grapes are usually still more acid.

SOME CHARACTERISTICS FROM WINES OF THE SAME GRAPE ACCORDING TO THE FERMENTATION SYSTEM

	Wines fermented from whole grapes			Wines fermented from stemless grapes	
	"Lágrima"	"Corazón"	"Repisado-Press"	"Destemmed"	"Pressed"
Alcohol	11.6º	12.4º	12.3º	12.5º	12.6º
Tartaric acid	4.2	3.8	3.6	4.5	4.7
Colour (relative)	1	3	4	2	2.5

During the fermentation process in the Rioja, for each litre of must, 105 grammes of CO_2 gas is given off, occupying 54 litres.

Fermentation lasts for a period which is inverse to the temperature. Some alcohol is always lost in relation to the temperature.

Temperature reached	Days of fermentation	Alcohol lost
20	30	0.1º
25	17	0.2º
30	12	0.5º
35	8	1.0º
40	6	2.5º

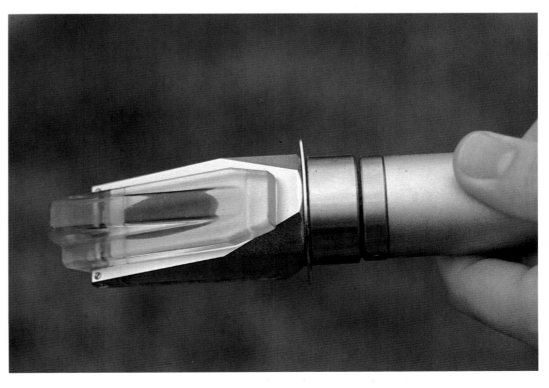

Refractometer

WHITE WINES

The fermentation process for white wines is strongly conditioned by the timing of the harvest. When red wine is made in the Rioja, wineproducers wait until the grape is completely ripe. Being a marginal area the red grape takes a long time in forming all the colour necessary in its skin. This does not occur in Aragón or Castilla where the grapes form an intense red colour before the harvest. On the other hand, when white wine is made, one can opt for bringing the harvest forward or putting it back. In both cases, the wine will be white, but with the early harvest it will be pale, acid, fresh, fruity and with low alcohol. By delaying the harvest, the wine will be more insipid, smoother, with golden tones and hardly any fruity aromas. We have to remember that white grapes are more delicate than the red varietes; they are susceptible to attack by moulds during ripening; this can spoil them, producing wines with an excessively golden colour. Therefore, in the Rioja, the harvest date can give us different types of white wines. But the dual nature of white Rioja wines does not depend only on the harvest but basically on present-day tastes. One part of the market seeks Rioja white wines aged in oak for a few years - golden wines with a tendency towards an oxidised taste. It is a minority choice. A large group of consumers look for pale, fruity, young wines without a taste of oak. Market trends have forced bodegas to produce these wines. In complete agreement with this, we can also say that young, fruity wines are attained exclusively from the Viura grape, older, golden wines with Malvasia or white Garnacha. To sum up:

YOUNG, FRESH WHITE WINES. Early harvest, Viura variety, fermentation at 22° C.

GOLDEN, AGEABLE WHITE WINES. Late harvest, Garnacha or Malvasía varieties and fermentation at 25-30° C.

The white Viura variety is a grape which has important qualities for white Rioja wines, even for sparkling wines, while Malvasia and Garnacha have fewer possibilities due their tendency to produce wine with an oxidised, rancid taste.

Maderisation of wine is the oxidation of some white wines increasing the intensity of the colour until it is similar to wood. At the same time, the wine acquires a rough taste similar to the astringency of wood tannin.

Destemming makes wines finer, smoother and more delicate.

There are also two methods of preparing white wines. One is the craft method and the other is industrial. The craft method is based on the use of stone vats.

When a wineproducer makes white wine, he harvests white grapes and places them whole in the vat, turning them over from time to time. After a few hours he opens the tap or "canilla", situated in the lower part of the vat, through which a white must flows and ferments in underground vats of oak or cement. Red grapes are thrown onto the pressed white grapes (the pressing is never severe); thereafter the white wine is made in the same way as the red. Some wineproducers have a small de-stemming machine through which the grapes pass, obtaining, after the tap is opened, a larger amount of must.

It is easy to understand that in vats with a higher capacity than 20,000 Kg, the wineproducer must turn the grapes over gently and, therefore, neither skins nor stems should be removed violently. This results in very fine wines. The disadvantage in some areas near Najerilla, where the subsoil is so cool that grapes excessively poor in tannin are produced. This causes incorrect fermentation, and the disease known as "gras" or "graisse".

Industrial processing consists of working much larger amounts of grapes with a tendency towards continuous systems. The most important thing is to know the extent to which the grape juice should be worked in order to obtain wines which continue to be fresh and light-coloured.

The system with the most continuous process consists of the initial separation of the stem. Afterwards, the slightly injured grape goes on to a vibrating stainless-steel sieve which separates the "yema" (yolk) or "flor" (flower) must, which only requires gravity separation. The partially-drained solid mass goes on to a continuous press which exerts little pressure, separating more must. The pasty mass now goes on to a continuous horizontal press which separates three types of liquid depending on the pressure, the final liquid being unsuitable for wine-making.

There is a non-continuous system which gives high quality; it is based on a system of wooden cages. The pressed grapes are transferred to cement containers which are lined internally with cages made of wooden boards. The must drains for some hours and the thick substance which remains is emptied into "horizontal presses". These are horizontal cylindrical cages, the bottoms of which are joined mechanically, squeezing out the liquid.

These liquids are separated and are of different quality. They are white grape musts and are still cloudy. If they are left to ferment with this cloudy appearance, the wine becomes rough. The cleaner the white grape must, the better the wine obtained.

To clean the must, deposit-removing operations are carried out. The must is placed in vats for one day. During this time the solid materials that make the must cloudy precipitate. Separation is made by pumping the clean must and transferring it to another container where it ferments. This is called the "debourbage" or racking operation.

Stems are used as organic fertiliser in vineyards.

ROSÉ WINES

The market for rosé wines from the Rioja has experienced a serious depression, as has been the case for all rosé wines throughout the world. Today a slight increase in demand is becoming apparent.

At present, out of every one hundred litres of Rioja marketed, 75 litres are red, 12 litres are white and 13 litres are rosé. Although the most highly appreciated is Rioja red, the classic product of the region, there is a growing demand for whites and a slight tendency of increase in demand for rosé. In terms of red wine, there is no competition for the Rioja in the productive areas of Spain. On the other hand competition with whites and rosés from other areas is very strong, in quantity and quality.

On many occasions we have heard it said that the Rioja should concentrate on the production of reds on an exclusive basis and that whites and rosés should be made in other regions of Spain which are better adapted. This opinion is not well-founded.

Red wines are more sought after and only a few regions are able to make excellent reds. Others have dedicated their efforts to making whites and rosés, however it is more difficult to make good red wine; whites and rosés represent an intermediate level. On the other hand, a region such as the Rioja, whose reputation for excellent reds is widely recognised, could, should it wish to do so, make the best whites and rosés in Spain. In any wine competition it would become evident that not only are the reds of the Rioja the best but that the whites and rosés of this region are also of high quality.

The preparation of rosés is very dependent on the ripening of the grape. The colour contributed by the grape to the wine only exists in the skin while the pulp is white. Theoretically, although very red in appearance, if we peeled some grapes and took out the pulp, the result would be a white wine. Alternatively, if we break open the grape and the pulp (or must) remains in contact with the skins, the liquid will absorb the colour slowly.

From mid-August to mid-October, the skin colour of the gape intensifies. If we harvest to make rosé in mid-September, the wine would be paler than if harvested in October. Here, the state of ripeness of the grape and the maceration time of the must with the skins play a very important role. The maceration time varies from very little for ripe grapes to several days for less ripe grapes.

For example, below we have indicated the maceration period necessary to obtain the same rosé colour in different areas of the Rioja in a normal vintage, using the red Garnacha grape:

Locality	Alcohol	Maceration time
San Adrián	13.6°	Instantaneous separation
Ausejo	12.9°	Six hours
Cenicero	12.3°	Twelve hours (Rosé of "one night")
Fonzaleche	11.2°	Two days

Not only a similar colour is obtained but the difference can be noted on the palate. The rosé of Fonzaleche is in contact for two days, during which the must not only absorbs colour from the skins, but also other substances which make it agreeable and aromatic. Alternatively, rosé made from unripened grapes tends to have an agreeable level of acidity.

For the traditional methods, wineproducers use the old open vats. Rioja growers usually have different types of grapes in their vineyard. When they wish to make rosé, they first harvest the white grapes with a small proportion of red. They are left in the vat for a few hours and the next day are pressed gently. After opening the tap in the bottom of the vat, the must flows out and ferments in underground oak or cement vats. Once the must has been extracted, the wineproducer proceeds to harvest the red grapes. He puts them into the vat on top of the pressed juice and leaves them to ferment according to the typical process for red wine.

The industrial bodega of the Rioja operates in a similar fashion, but with machinery that allows a certain continuity in the process. In principle, they only process red grapes if they are from an area where ripeness is hard to achieve; white and red grapes if they are from a sunny area of the Rioja.

The stems are then removed from this mass of harvested grapes. They are crushed slightly and submitted to a continuous process with stainless-steel vibrators which separate the must from the solid matter. Alternatively, the mass of must and skins are transferred to draining or maceration tanks. Here the duration of contact between the liquid and skins is controlled. Once the must has taken on the desired tone of rosé, it is transferred to other containers where the "burbas" or solid suspended matter is decanted for one day. The must, which now has a bright colour, is sent to the containers for fermentation.

Fermentation bay in La Rioja Alta, S.A.
In fermentation, and only in fermentation,
stainless steel is the ideal material.

Pressed Garnacha grape. It can be observed that the pulp keeps its transparency as if it were a white grape and the colour stays in the skin.

Once the maceration with skins has been achieved, the process is identical to that of white wines. It is essential to prevent temperatures from exceeding 25° C. High temperatures cause the fruity flavours to be lost.

Although red wines mature in time, rosé and whites wines are consumed very young to take advantage of their freshness, aroma and fruity taste. No more than twenty years ago it was traditional in the Rioja to allow white and rosé wines to age in cask in the same way as reds. Today, old rosé wines are a minority taste, the tendency is to market them in their first or second year.

The varieties of Rioja grapes dedicated to rosé wines are basically red Garnacha or blends of red Garnacha, Tempranillo and white Viura.

The maceration time for extracting colour from the skins does not need to be the same for each variety. Garnacha produces better rosés with longer maceration and Tempranillo gives better quality with a very short maceration.

The following chart shows the results of different maceration times of the skins with the must in order to achieve rosé in Tirgo:

Contact time	Alcohol	Fixed tartaric acidity	Relative colour	TASTING
0 (instantaneous)	11.1°	7.1	1	Good. Rough aftertaste.
12 hours	11.3°	6.8	1.3	Very agreeable, hard on palate.
24 hours	11.1°	6.3	1.8	Very agreeable, soft.
36 hours	11.2°	6.4	2.1	The best aroma, colour and taste.
48 hours	11.0°	6.2	2.4	Slightly insipid.

It is very important for the enologist to calculate the right maceration time, as this is essential to give the wine the precise colour, aromas, softness, roughness, etc.

In 1972 wine regulations clearly specified the difference between red, "claret" and rosé (red wine is total fermentation with skins, "claret" is fermented for a short time with the skins and rosé is fermented without skins). Traditionally, the expression "Rioja claret" exists from almost medieval times when the English sought wines with different hues. For them, Portuguese wine was "black", while the zone of the Gulf of Gascogne (Bordeaux and Rioja) was the area for "clarets", although these were strictly speaking, reds.

An external curtain of water allows the fermentation temperature to be maintained.

YEASTS

Yeasts are microbes which carry out fermentation, transforming sugared must into wine; a liquid with alcohol and without sugar.

Yeasts live in our environment and arrive at the bodega adhering to the skin of the grapes. Afterwards, they multiply in the must and act energetically.

Beer, bread, sake, ketir and kumis are food products made with yeasts.

Yeasts are not pathogenic elements for man, at least not those found on grapes, in vineyards and bodegas. On the other hand, they themselves represent a food of enormous value, they are rich in nitrogen and vitamins. A fermenting must would be much more nutritious than still must or wine.

There are several types of yeasts which cause the fermentation of Rioja wine. Those which begin the fermentation are always yeasts which take advantage of the air present in the must. When they have consumed the air they die and those which do not need air, i.e., those which cause the fermentation, become active. These strictly fermenting yeasts belong to the Saccharomyces type.

The size of yeasts ranges from three to six thousandths of a millimetre. When grapes are pressed, there are usually fifty yeasts per cubic centimetre. In the middle of the fermentation process, there are one hundred million per cubic centimetre.

Formerly, yeasts (of which there are many types) were classified according to shape, as observed under a microscope; but today it is necessary to resort to physiological tests in order to classify them. Of the five hundred types associated with fermentation and food which have been classified throughout the world, only fifty are to be found in the vineyards, bodegas and wines. Of these, in La Rioja, we could say that only about five species are of any importance. We have found that when wines are of high quality, the following species are found in the fermentation of Rioja wine:

Initially, Metsnikowa pulcherrima.

Until half way through the process, Saccharomyces rosei.

From half way to the end of the process, Saccharomyces cerevisiae.

These names are certainly very strange for the uninitiated but nevertheless, even if technicians did not know them, it would be possible to obtain (in general terms) the same excellent wines which our predecessors were able to produce.

The yeasts which make red wines of the Rioja are the same as those which produce whites and rosés.

In some cases, when the harvested grapes are very cold on arrival at the bodega, or when they have been exposed to heavy autumn rain and their yeast has been washed away, yeasts are provided by means of a "pie de cuba". This consists of keeping a small amount of the same must from another part of the bodega, at about 25° C, to activate the yeasts and then transfer them to the mass of harvested grapes which require fermentation.

There was a time when it was believed that yeasts were a prodigious element and that by incorporating a Rioja yeast, for example, in musts from other regions, Rioja wine could be obtained. Tests were even made with a yeast from Jerez in musts from La Mancha in order to obtain Rioja wine. This change is not possible as the type of wine is influenced by a variety of grape, its genetic characteristics and environment.

Some yeasts spoil bottled wines. When a kind of "cream" appears on the surface of a wine in bottle, this means that the wine has a low alcohol content and the "cream" is in fact millions of yeasts cells. This could happen in any weak Rioja red wine.

In other regions, wine is conserved with "la madre" in the vats. This term defines the yeasts which transform the wine but also defend it from the attack of bacteria which make it vinegary.

Bottled Rioja wines withstand attack by yeasts. Reds are seldom attacked, which is one advantage of our Rioja. On the other hand, whites and rosés are affected by yeasts which produce sediment in the form of small balls, (millions of agglutinated yeasts), or a powdery sediment or a general cloudiness. For this reason, whites and rosés are filtered before bottling, but not Rioja reds.

If yeasts live basically on the sugar present in the grape, one could ask how they react in wine which does not contain sugar. The answer is simple. Yeasts prefer to feed on sugar, but when there is a lack of it some yeasts (not all) feed on the alcohol, especially when the bottle has a large air space or when the cork is not up to standard.

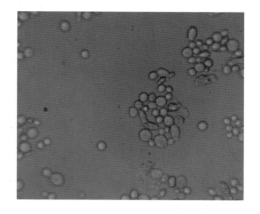

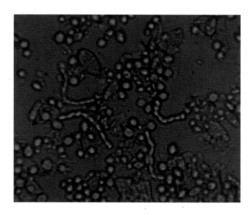

Fermentation of Rioja wine seen under 1200 times magnification.

**SHAPE OF THE YEASTS WHICH OCCUR IN FERMENTATIONS OF RIOJA WINE
(In wines of the highest quality)**

AT THE BEGINNING

MIDDLE

END

DEVATTING

Drawing off, or devatting, is the term used to describe the operation of separating the residual parts of the grapes from the liquid, once the red wine has been fermented.

Clearly, this operation does not occur in whites or rosés, as these ferment without maceration of the skins or stems.

During fermentation, when red wine is being made, the musts and grape skins macerate together. After fermentation, the solid parts are separated. However, the wine is still not completely fermented and the process continues in the absence of the skins until it is completed. In December, the smaller sediments, which are tartrates and dead yeast, are removed when the wine is racked.

The problem associated with devatting is to know when to carry it out. This is usually very late in regions where enology is not advanced. In the Rioja, its importance is well-recognised, depending on the degree of ripening; whether early or late.

In general terms, during the making of young wine with whole grapes, the grapes seem to sink and foam appears in the corners of the vat.

With destemmed grapes, which is the classical system used in Rioja bodegas, the moment is decided by a density meter control.

An early devatting attains wine with little colour, a strong fixed acidity and a fruity aroma. A late devatting gives red wine with colour but less fixed acidity and less fruity aromas. A very late devatting means, once again, a loss of colour, insipid taste and very little fixed acidity.

The enologist acts by taking into consideration the quality the climate has given the grape each year. If the ripening process has been correct and generous and the enologist devats early, then despite this, the wine will have acquired colour. But if the harvested grapes are green due to a lack of ripeness, it is necessary to put off devatting so that the wine can acquire colour.

Wineproducers devat by "bleeding" wine which flows freely. Later, by forcing the drawing off of more wine by turning the grapes over. The remaining mass is then removed from inside the vat by men with pitchforks and taken in baskets to the press.

Industrial bodegas extract wine which flows freely. The mass can also be extracted by workers with pitchforks; or by mixing with a little wine it can be removed with the use of a suction pump.

A bundle of vine twigs, held with stones inside the vat, acts as a natural filter during devatting.

PRESSING

Pomace, which is the skin, pips and stems of the fermented grape, still contains wine after devatting; it must be recovered. To do this, the pomace is subjected to a pressing operation which consists simply of exercising pressure on the wet mass in order to separate the liquid from solids. The pressure is gradual and the wine flows little by little, the first amounts being of good quality, the following having more colour and roughness. The final amounts are very rough and have very little alcohol; the wine has already mixed with the water contained in the stems.

There are very few villages in the Rioja, where traditional methods are used, which have presses. Where they exist they are usually of the vertical type moved by hand or with an electric motor. The wineproducers take turns to press their pomace. Sometimes, there is some delay and the pomace is pressed when it is hot and aired resulting in a pressed wine which is a little vinegary.

The initial wine obtained from pressing is of good quality but those obtained with intermediate or heavy pressing are of lower quality. This, technically known as "obligatory wine delivery", is a measure imposed by the government whereby wine, which does not reach minimum quality levels, is sent for distillation.

Industrial bodegas work with several different types of presses. Some of them still use vertical presses similar to those used by wineproducers. Others use a horizontal rotary press and still others a continuous press or the rotation of a helical screw-spindle.

Quality is influenced not only by the use of pressure, but also by the quality of the materials with which the press is made. Wood and stainless steel are considered as being fine materials, while iron has a negative effect.

For obvious reasons, to make white and rosé wine, the skins and stems are removed before fermentation. Therefore, the pressing operation is carried out with fresh grapes and the liquid extracted is must. Musts which flow after the effect of the heavier pressure are of poor quality, inadequate for making wine. They have a low alcohol level, a brown colour and a herbaceous taste. These fermented musts are also used for the "obligatory wine delivery"

Horizontal stainless steel and wooden press.

←
Removing the solid paste, after devatting.

DECEMBER RACKING

Until the month of December, it can be said that Rioja wine is not completely fermented, whether it is red, white or rosé. When the wine is devatted, it is still sweet. Later, it slowly begins to lose sugar through controlled fermentation until it becomes "dry", in other words, without a sweet taste.

When Rioja wines are dry, they still contain one or two grammes per litre of sugar, but this is normal and does not cause problems of taste or stability.

Until December the yeast lives in the wines, consuming sugar. Then, the yeast dies and falls to the bottom of the tank. This is helped by the month's cold temperatures. It is said that the wine clears. Theoretically, it is now ready for consumption, but the yeasts which fall to the bottom of the tank together with insoluble tartrate crystals or very small vegetable particles are very rich in nitrogen and vitamins. In addition, the dead yeast can break up and release yellowish colour into the wine.

We must remember that dead yeast in a 25,000-litre tank of wine can mean a thousand litres of organic matter. If racking is done early, the dead yeast having been recently deposited, the wine has a hard, acid, fruity taste; but is a fresh and fruity aroma,

perhaps a little rough. On the other hand, by putting this separation off until January, as Rioja wineproducers recommend (until the first full moon of January), the yeast may have broken up. Bacteria grows among the yeasts and the colour of the wine is less vivid; the wine less acid, less fresh and fruity with a tendency towards indistinct odours and tastes.

We might ask the following question: What has the moon to do with December racking, bearing in mind that it is typical in the Rioja for wineproducers to rack at the first full moon in January? We can offer two explanations. One of them is that the first full moon usually coincides with high atmospheric pressure. This means frost and the wine is cold. However, we understand that many farming operations show that during the life cycle of moulds and fungi, such as yeast, some phases of the moon stimulate their growth and activity while others have the opposite effect. It is possible that Rioja wine producers have detected over the centuries that in specific phases of the moon the activity of yeast is very limited and offers a good opportunity to separate a large amount of clean wine.

The dirty sediment, separated in this racking operation, is called lees and is a liquid very rich in organic matter. It is usually channelled to the tartaric acid extraction industry or for the recovery of alcohol, through the "obligatory wine delivery" system.

Cloudy wine in racking.

MACHINERY USED IN THE BODEGA

Machinery used in bodegas is very simple and dates from antiquity. Means, systems and concepts based on the principles used for wines and oils by the Greeks and Romans are still used today in the Rioja. The most complicated piece of machinery, perhaps, is the press. This has great similarity to the Roman "torculum". The expression "torco" is commonly used in the Rioja to describe the container into which must, or wine leaving the press, is poured.

We must consider the machinery used in bodegas in two large blocks:

Machinery for working grapes.
Machinery for working wine.

It may appear that some bodegas have an industrial appearance or automatic systems, but basic operations are controlled by the Control of Origin Regulating Council, according to traditional Rioja working methods.

The machinery involved in working grapes simply refers to the means necessary for transporting them from the fields to the fermentation vats and for removing the stems.

Bunches contain two usable parts: grapes and inert parts, i.e., stems.

The operations which are carried out from the moment the grapes arrive at the bodega require the following machinery:

1. A wormgear spindle, also called helical transporter or Archimedes spindle. This turns and transports the grapes, practically untouched, to the next machine which is the destemmer.
2. The destemmer gently separates the stems from the grapes and ejects the former, later used as a by-product, and channels the mass of stemless grapes towards the pump.
3. The pump sends the thick mass of grapes to the vats where they are to ferment. It can be understood that, given the density of the liquid and the certain semi-liquid aspect (as there is must with skins and pips), a simple centrifuge or impeller pump is not enough. The pumps used are slow rotary piston or vane pumps made from materials which are unaffected by the must and channel the harvested grapes through 20 cm diameter tubes. The tubes are made from stainless steel or reinforced plastic.

Once the wine has been fermented, it is necessary, before racking, to use a simple centrifuge pump to separate the solid mass of skins which floats on top. We could say that this is machine number four.

After pumping the wine over the mass of skins, it is extracted by means of a tap situated in the lower part of the vat. The wine-soaked skins are then channeled to a pump, very similar to the one used for harvested grapes, to take this mass to the press. This pump can be called, according to the order of operations, machine number five and the press, number six.

The press may be vertical, horizontal or continuous.

Both the vertical and horizontal presses are structures made of strengthened wood. One of the slats, in the vertical press, squashes the mass and the wine flows through the bars. Or, there are two slats which come together and flatten the solid mass, squeezing out the wine.

The continuous press has a perforated metal casing in the form of a horizontal cylinder. On the axis there is a very strong screwspindle which receives and transports the solid mass, pushing it against an outlet gate, which is kept semi-closed by a counterweight or hydraulic system.

Destemmer and press.

Conveyor belt for removing the lees to the press.

Press.

AGEING

HISTORY OF THE OAK

Considered as a fine material, "par excellence", for containing wine, we should nevertheless be critical in its use. Only in this way can we ensure future use coherent with the search for quality.

There are two contrary reasons why oak has become the most important material rest and transport.

With the arrival of the 18th Century, the growing obsession for quality created a demand for hermetic seals which would facilitate rough journeys by land and extremely long sea crossings without a negative effect on the wine caused by external circumstances such as cold or pressure. At least there was a demand for some form of container which would withstand these elements better than jars or leather wineskins. So wood became popular, and of all the wood available the most innocuous was chosen - oak.

If we look back to the origins of modern enology we can see that our arguments in favour of oak as a tradition or as a means of ageing really only serve to tie enological evolution down to the technical necessities of two hundred years ago. It is true, of course, that in many cases this idea is convenient and worthy of promoting, but it does not mean that we should not open our eyes and compare our present technological means with those of the past. The old bodegas used oak to preserve their wine in cellars or caves for at least two or three years simply because the cold of two winters helped the spontaneous clearing enabling them to offer the wine in better condition. They saw that some vintages could only be kept two years but that others, (those of the best climatology), could be preserved for more. The oak vat or barrel did not age the wine, but it conveyed the idea of ageing. Their aim was to age or keep the wine in order to make it clear of residues.

In addition, the casks and barrels were very convenient for handling when shipping. It is hardly surprising that in nautical weight a ton is a thousand kilos, more or less the weight of the typical "tonneau" of Bordeaux wine (900 litres). One is led to think that the original aim was not to age the wine but to facilitate its stabilisation and transport.

After the bottle, oak has maintained its position as the ideal cellar container for processing, production and ageing.

Today, it must be recognised that many regions, which have regulated their systems of winemaking and ageing by basing them on oak, have done this out of an interest in maintaining a tradition of past techniques.This seems perfectly fair if one considers that at present only 75% of the wine produced in the world is consumed and that selling at a low price is dangerously easy. We can only defend ourselves by creating an image which may be debatable for technical reasons where oak is concerned, but it is ultimately beneficial to the vine-growing areas.

It is hugely paradoxical that we should call a material "fine", "par excellence", that influences the wine's colour, aroma, taste and composition. It may not be harmful and it is certainly traditional, but by no means is it inert.

In our case, and perhaps in that of other specialists in vines and wines, it is a fact that certain forest polymers help us in our profession but on the other hand create more complications and worries than the problems caused by the wine itself. We are referring of course to oak and cork.

We talk a lot of special corks, of first grade, second grade etc., or of French oak, American oak, sawn, split etc., but if we reflect on our words many of our specialists in this matter are simply full of pseudotechnical clichés, which is exactly the opposite to what society expects of us.

We have studied in certain depth, or at least such has been our intention, the significance of all these concepts from the enological point of view. From this starting point of doubt we have arrived at the conscious affirmation of the importance of the time spent by red Rioja wine in contact with oak.

Vigier Cellar, dating from 1890.

CONCERNING OAK AND CASKS

No other secondary material has become as important to the life of wine as oak.

Oak is not inert matter, its reciprocal relation with wine being in itself and by tradition beneficial to the consumer.

So much so that numerous regulations respecting quality wines focus the image of their products on the time the wines spend in oak casks.

For centuries, there have been regulations concerning oak and the shape of the cask. We still know very little today about oak in relation to its reaction with wine. The modern wine cellar hardly seems the place for the convex anatomy of the casks, which may have been functional in the past, but nowadays means harder work. But this is a price to be paid for wines which are valued, not only for their quality, but also for a certain image. A tendency to simplify could paradoxically complicate this overall image of quality, the presentation of which, reflects the many hours of work which are dedicated to its production.

Despite centuries of coexistence between wine and oak it is difficult to find any systematic, specific research amongst many vague theories.

Nevertheless, at times we think we know a great deal and become dogmatic, searching for a foothold where none is to be found.

Our intention here is not to expound a far-reaching study, but rather to try to put ideas into some kind of perspective, perhaps of possible use to specialists who, like ourselves, entertain serious doubts about the rhetoric surrounding oak and its relationship with wine.

Variants to be considered.

The oak used in wine casks can have the following variants:

a) Different species of oak.
b) Different growth habitats.
c) Different forestry techniques (regime, growth etc.).
d) Different types of cut (split or sawn).
e) Different seasoning periods for the cut wood.
f) Different stave thickness.
g) Different degree of scorching for bending.
h) Possibility of caulking or pore coverage by the barrel-maker.

After considering these parameters of such inexact evaluation we might ask ourselves: What do we know in technical terms about oak? Can an enologist venture to predict the response of a batch of oak casks to a certain wine?

It may be that, despite being specialists on the subject of oak and wine, we act:

1. routinely
2. in response to clichés
3. in blind faith regarding the prestige of the barrel-makers as craftsmen.

PARTS
AND DIMENSIONS

The Rioja cask is the Bordeaux model of 225 litres, a weight when empty of 55 Kg.
The dimensiones are:

Length . . . . 95 cm.
Thickness of the stave. . . . . 29 mm.
maximum diameter . . . . 70 cm.
Diameter of head. . . . . 57 cm.
Number of staves 27-28
Number of boards in bottom. 5-7
      Normally: 1 middle board
               2 lateral boards
               2 "chantreles"
Number of galvanised hoops 8

Making bungs which are changed for each racked cask.

THE CUTTING OF OAK
AND ITS INFLUENCE ON WINE

Studies on cutting

By the cross - section of an oak trunk we have tried to reconstruct the concepts of split and sawn oak.

H represents a cut and A a sawn section. As can be easily seen, by cutting the oak stave is longitudinally structured over the pith rays which are of perfectly impermeable wood. The cut surface is uneven but the wine scarcely penetrates the wood: so the transfer of tannin and washing are also reduced to a minimum.

Sawn oak, on the contrary, presents an apparently smooth surface but it has in fact a bristly outer area. It is very easily soaked and, having no impermeable longitudinal wall, is amply penetrated by wine, giving rise to strong impregnation and transfer of tannin and consequently needing heavy washing.

There is still a logical possibility of avoiding this risk by "treating" the interior surface of the sawn wood to reduce its permeability.

Diffusion of the wine

Through its behaviour in extension and depth, the chromatic performance of a red wine in different types of cuts and areas of oak is shown:

The drawing shows the penetration of red wine in a split stave (H) and a sawn stave (A).

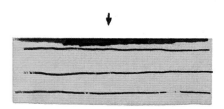

H

CROSS SECTION OF THE OAK TRUNK

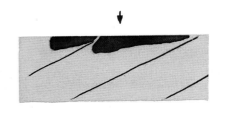

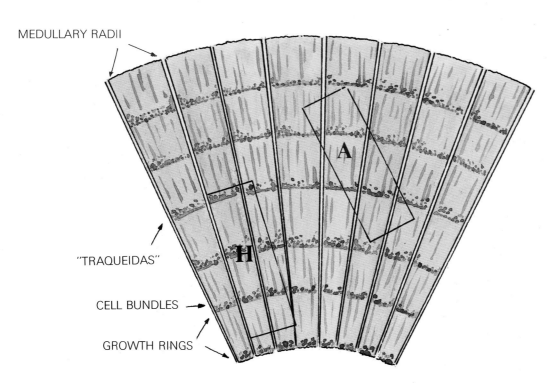

MEDULLARY RADII

"TRAQUEIDAS"

CELL BUNDLES

GROWTH RINGS

A

H SPLIT STAVE

A SAWN STAVE

SCORCHING STAVES

Scorching staves in order to curve them is an important operation, but is seldom considered in enology.

This scorching is not restricted merely to changes in surface colour but also, from what we have observed, affects a 50-cm length of the inside face of the stave and a thickness of 2 mm.

Despite the elasticity created by the heat, the stave acquires folds (under the effect of the curving strain), which can leave cavities 1-2 mm below the surface with a length of up to 5mm and a maximum gap of one millimetre. On the scorched face the strain of curving may also create exfoliations in the direction of the grain.

It is also quite logical to think that the change would be important with the heating of the vegetable elements causing a change in the anatomy. Folds and hollows are created which make the subsequent asepsis of the wood difficult.

So scorching implies a change in the texture of the oak which is in contact with the wine as well as an alteration in its elements through heating that may affect the quantity and quality of any transfer from the oak to the wine.

Experimental contribution

We kept Rioja white wines in contact with split staves of oak, some scorched normally and others scorched and planed in the burnt zone until the oak was clean.

One month later the wines underwent a study based on various parameters.

Colour change

Control wine
Wine in scorched staves
Wine in unscorched staves

The white wine which was kept in contact with the scorched oak intensified in colour.

Variation of tannin	Quantity of tannin
Control wine	Low
Wine in scorched staves	Moderate
Wine in clean staves	High.

Colour increases when the wine is in contact with scorched staves, but no increase of tannin is evident, so there is no harshness of taste.

The "Viña Arana" cellar and its twin "Viña Ardanza" contain a total of 20,600 Bordeaux shaped American oak casks.

Effect on the colour of the wine

The effect of the cask on the colour of red wine is reflected in the optical density measured after one month:

	Colour	Yellow	Red
Control wine	2.42	1.3	1.62
Wine in scorched oak	2.87	1.6	1.17
Wine in planed oak	8.0	1.4	1.60

The scorched oak surface transfers yellow colouring matter and retains some red.

Scorching the inside of oak staves for curving has an important effect on wines, at least in the first usage cycles of the cask.

This scorched oak surface becomes more porous in texture and has a higher liquid retention. However, wine that has penetrated the wood seems to resist souring.

The wine receives yellow chromatic elements and retains red ones. The most interesting result achieved is the identification of a taste definable by winetasters as "grasa" or "arpillera", noted in certain oaks after scorching and which is transmitted to the wine. We detected this defect in the first usage of certain batches of casks and now we have been able to determine the origin.

Alteration of wine residues

After the casks are emptied they are aired for two days and then washed with two litres of water. This water is later used to determine possible oxydisation of the wine in the wood. In scorched staves the level is 0.1 gm/l. and in clean ones 0.28 gm/l. demonstrating that scorching provides more resistance to residual wine.

Taste with scorched oak

This test was carried out in a laboratory, using oak samples of 10 x 5 x 2 cm, scorching them laterally and filling them with Rioja red wine of the 1985 vintage to a volume of 500 cc, hermetically sealed and tasted after ten days:

TASTING OF WINES IN CONTACT WITH SCORCHED OAK

Asturian oak . . . . taste and aroma defined by winetasters as "arpillera".
Allier oak . . . . slight contribution of indefined taste.
Limousine oak . . . . Smooth taste similar to "arpillera" or "grasa".
Nevers oak . . . . very light, strange taste.

In summary it is very interesting to have found the reason for the taste of "arpillera" in certain wines. We have occasionally found a taste definable as "arpillera", even "grasa" in some wines. The reason is an excess scorching of the oak in new casks.

Inter-relations between air, oak and wine.

Our knowledge of these inter-relations is as yet imperfect. We can give them a structure based on studies carried out by various researchers and by ourselves. The oak is a barrier between wine and air.

I. Passage and microdiffusion of atmospheric air through the oak into the wine.

II. Transfer from oak to wine of:
      a) Lignin
      b) Polyphenols
      c) Enzymes: Glycosidase
                  Tannase
                  Pepsidase
                  Polyphenoloxidase

III. Diffusion of wine into the atmosphere through oak.

For example, with sawn staves all these functions would be intense but with split staves they would be attenuated.

Preservation variables

There are also the following preservation variables:

A. Atmospheric humidity

B. Degree of exposure to wine of the casks

In any cask, low atmospheric humidity stimulates function III. Prolonged exposure to wine, of more than five years, attenuates all three functions.

The role of alcohol

Alcohol in wine acts in the following ways:

A. Hydrolysing lignin in the oak and giving an aroma of balsam.

B. It extracts non-flavinoid polyphenols (acids and aldehydes) of the benzoic and cinnamic series.

C. It extracts hydrolysed tannins, giving gallic and elagic acids.

This elagic acid released by oak into the wine helps prevent the existence of microbes.

Colour retention

The retention of anthocyanins of red wine in different types of wood has been studied with their subsequent removal through liquid.

Wood	Sawn cut	Split cut
Oak	+ + + +	+ +
Alder	+ + +	+
Chestnut	+ + +	+

This demonstrates that new sawn oak extracts the red colour from a red wine but the majority of this can later be removed from the wood by washing with water.

VARIATIONS IN WINE

Our bodega in Labastida (1,200 casks).

Commercially-available types of oak

We have studied the behaviour of the same wine in oak casks from different commercial origins, all of which are of sawn oak with staves of 28-30 mm.

In a wine cellar in Haro, the wine was put in to cask in July 1976 and taken out in January 1978, undergoing two rackings.

The wine in question was red of 15°. The results after drawing off from these new casks were as follows:

Cask	Lustre	Potassium mg./l.	pH	Tartaric g/l.	Malic g/l.
A	+++	1.008	3.35	3.6	0
B	+·+++	760	3.25	4.1	0
C	+++	820	3.25	4.0	0
D	++++	630	3.25	4.2	0.2

Cask	Oak aroma	Oak taste	Colour of the wine
A	++++	++++	Low and of old appearance
B	+++	++	Normal, old appearance
C	+	+	Low and young
D	+	—	Normal and old appearance

We can see that the influence on the composition of wine is important, but by tasting more than by analysis:

    Aroma
    Taste
    Colour

The effect is such, that a young wine in different types of oaks, when drawn off, gives the sensation of being of different ages.

116

Another study was undertaken to compare the behaviour of a wine in wood from the same origin, already exposed to wine, but with staves of 20 and 28 mm.

After eight months, including one racking, the results were as follows:

	Control	28 mm.	20 mm.
Alcohol	12.6°	12.54°	12.50°
Volatile acidity	0.38	0.47	0.66
Colour (1)	2.1	1.9	2.2
Loss/decanting	—	0.7%	1.9%

Oak and steel

Anthocyanins are the red colour of purple grapes.

Using standard research techniques for the decrease of anthocyanins in red wine in different vats/casks we have tried to determine their behaviour in young red Tempranillo wine from the Rioja with a pH of 3.55, alcohol content of 12.7° and 488 mg/l of anthocyanins.

Wine is preserved in a new sawn cask with 28-mm staves, whilst another portion of the same wine is preserved in stainless steel for one year. In the second year the same operation is carried out with the used cask from the previous wine. The wine is drawn off from the casks every six months.

Wine	Initial anthocyanins	After a year in steel	After a year in oak
1980	488	378 (−22%)	462 (−5%)
1981	612	483 (−21%)	556 (−9%)

Practically the same criteria are met here as by other authors. New oak defends against the drop in anthocyanins in Tempranillo red wine. Stainless steel facilitates the loss of part of the grape colour in red wine. Oak, particularly when new, helps it resist the loss for a longer period.

Content of total tannins

In sawn oak casks with 28-mm staves a study was carried out on the total tannin enrichment of white wine in a new cask. Also, in another five year old cask manufactured by the same cooper.

Tannins	Initial tannins	Final tannins	After one year
		New cask	5-year-old cask
	1.32 g./l.	1.97 g./l.	1.58 g./l.

Logically, the young oak increases the tannin in the wine.

Colour loss

In several harvests, we have considered variations in colour intensity after being kept for six months in a new cask and a cask of more than five years old. The results are taken from destemmed red wine from the northern part of the Rioja.

	C.I. Initial colour	C.I. New oak	C.I. Old oak
1981	2.1	2.1	1.8
1982	1.9	1.8	1.6
1983	2.0	1.9	1.8
1984	1.45	1.5	1.3
1985	1.6	1.53	1.4

Except in the case of the 1981 harvest, the colour intensity falls in all the wines, attenuated in new oak and intensely in old.

New oak allows the grape colour to remain in the wine for a longer period but increases the astringent taste. The specialist's task is to choose an oak which will help sustain the colour whilst causing less astringency.

(1) This value indicates intensity of colour. Red wines have a range of 6 in young wine to 1.5 in very old. A cask with thin 20 mm staves, accelerates the processes at work on the wine.

FIRST YEAR EVOLUTION

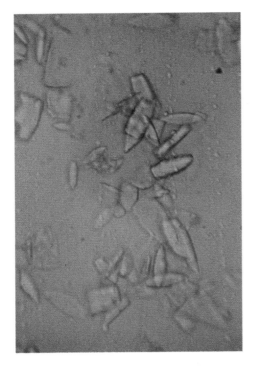

Tartrate deposits

In order to consider, stage by stage, the transformations which take place in Rioja wines during the first year of their life, one has to take into account the standards of the Regulating Council of the Control of Origin of the Rioja, which in 1976, defined periods for keeping wine in barrel and bottle.

Therefore, when reference is made to the first year in the life of a wine, it has to be borne in mind that, after being kept for some months in a large vat, the wine is transferred to oak casks and continues to be kept in this kind of container during its second year.

There is intense activity in the wine during its first year, for various reasons:

Sugar residues.
Destruction of the malic acid.
Sedimentation of the crystalline matter.

The crystalline matter which is formed in wine consists of natural salts, which are dissolved in the grape but become insoluble once alcohol is formed. However, this solidifying is a slow process, coinciding with cold periods. Over a period of time these crystals are deposited in the cask until the wine is considered stable and free from further risk of throwing a deposit.

Two types of crystals are precipitated in wines: potassium bitartrate (cream of tartrate) and lime tartrate. They are very similar in shape (drawings and photographs are shown) but there are differences in their characteristics. Potassium bitartrate dissolves with heat, has a slightly acid taste and usually precipitates in the wine during the first winter. Lime tartrate, however, usually precipitates by the second or third winter, has no acid taste and does not dissolve with heat. It is an annoying component, as it can appear in old bottled wine.

Although the colour is strictly speaking a transparent yellow, it occasionally takes on a wine-coloured, purplish appearance.

Sugar remains in the wine during the first year. It is a remnant of the grape sugar. These remnants are usually small in quantity, less than two grammes per litre, and the yeasts, with little remaining strength, slowly consume them. There are two periods in the year during which the yeasts are active in processed wines. One is Spring, coinciding with the flowering of the vine, the other Autumn, shortly before the harvest.

Another characteristic is that the maximum temperature in the cellars is reached in September, not July, the month of maximum atmospheric temperature.

The third factor regarding the activity of wine during its first year is malolactic deacidification or malolactical fermentation. It consists of the transformation of the malic acid into lactic acid and CO_2 gas.

Grapes contain various acids naturally:

Tartaric, characteristic of the grape . . . . 4.0 g./l.
Malic, characteristic of the apple . . . . 1.5 g./l.
Citric, characteristic of the lemon . . . . 0.2 g./l.

Malic acid gives wine a sharp flavour known as "greenness". For this reason enologists refer to a technique based on a natural element in grapes, the lactic bacteria which consumes this acid and transforms it into the much more agreeable lactic acid and CO_2 gas. This is the malolactical deacidification. It is carried out early in the northern part of the Rioja, later in the central region and is not necessary in the Southern areas. Here, the grapes are exposed to a lot of sunlight, giving greater maturity resulting in less malic acid in the wine.

Malolactical deacidification is favoured by taking care that the wine does not get cold and by avoiding racking or sulphuring.

When wine goes through malolactical deacidification it changes in the following ways:

a) The volatile acidity is raised by one tenth (normal rise of 50%).

b) The fixed acidity falls by five tenths (a fall of 10%).

c) Some colour is lost (15%).

d) The wine obtains a softer flavour with weak transitory bubbling.

←
Racking in the "Viña Ardanza" cellar.

Racking requires care, good judgment and experience.

SECOND YEAR
EVOLUTION

Throughout its second year Rioja wine is kept in oak casks with a capacity of 225 litres.

The changes undergone by the wine are, to a large extent, dictated by the nature of the oak.

These changes can be expressed as:

Crystalline transformations.

Transformations in colour.

Changes caused by racking.

Chemical changes.

As in the wine's first year of life, during the second the phenomenon of crystal formation continues, as does their precipitation to the bottom of the cask. In the second year the precipitation is fundamentally due to lime tartrate. The intensity of the process mainly coincides with cold periods, occurring therefore during the second winter.

In theory, specialists used to think that two winters would be sufficient for the spontaneous stabilizing of the wine. During the first, the potassium bitartrate precipitates and in the second the calcium tartrate. Thus a wine aged some twenty months would be ready for bottling. But the real situation is different and there are wines which can precipitate some tartrate crystals even in their fourth winter. This risky phenomenon occurs especially when, during the summer, the wine is kept in vessels lined with "alumbres". In this case the wine loses tartrate in winter only to take it back from the walls in the summer heat.

The transformations in the colour of the wine are profound. Wine in casks undergoes extreme changes, especially in the second year.

The colour of red wines is due to two fundamental elements:

1. Red-coloured elements or anthocyanins.

2. Yellow-coloured elements or tannins.

New wine is very rich in anthocyanins or red colour. After a year up to 50% is lost, and afterwards some is regained.

In cask the red colour fades and the yellow is intensified, mainly because of tannin filtering from the oak.

We can fix at 100, as a relative unit, the intensity of colour in a new wine. At the end of the first year the figure falls to 35%, rising to 45% by the end of the second year. This rise is due to absortion of tannin from the oak.

At the beginning of the second year the red elements can be 0.2 g/l., falling to 0.07 g/l. by the end of that year.

In contrast, the tannins or yellow elements are at 1.5 g/l. at the beginning of the second year, reaching approximately 1.7 g/l. at the end of the year if there is intense use of wood, or 2 g/l. if the wood is new.

So in cask the wine passes from clear red to ruby red as well as assimilating elements from the oak.

During its time in cask the wine clears itself spontaneously and inactive solid matter (plant residue, bacteria and dead yeast) settles at the bottom, leaving the wine clean and occasionally bright. If the wine were not separated from these elements it would eventually become cloudy again. For this reason the wine is racked off every three or four months and poured into clean, dried casks. However, not all the wine is drawn off, a small amount being left at the bottom. This is the sedimentary matter which makes cloudy wine and is logically rejected for use in quality wine. Each time the wine is drawn off several litres of sediment are separated.

In the racking process the wine receives a certain amount of air in its passage from one container to another, sustaining the liveliness of the red colour of the anthocyanins.

There is, however, another reason why wine can only stay in one container for less than six months. Oak is a material with only slight permeability. It eventually becomes soaked in wine, some of which evaporates through the pores, at the same time permitting the entrance of air. In consequence the wine loses volume, even in a closed cask, and a pocket of air is formed which could later oxidise the wine. Periodic drawing off of the wine avoids a dangerous increase in the volume of this air pocket.

There also exists two interesting types of chemical processes:

Esterifications.

Oxidations.

Esterification is the very slow combination of wine acids with alcohol. Basically these are tartaric acid, lactic acid, succinic acid, etc. with alcohol (ethanol). After some time in cask they react in very small proportions and produce compounds like ethyl tartrate, ethyl lactate etc. One can occasionally notice a certain "cheesy" aroma in some old Rioja wine. It is caused by the formation of ethyl lactate. The quantities are very small but the aromas produced are rather distinctive.

· Oxidation in the cask is due to the very slow diffusion of air through the oak, producing a limited amount of oxidation, mainly of the alcohol which turns into aldehyde. This has a special aroma (these are the elements which are thought to produce the aroma of Sherry and Montilla wines). This kind of oxidation in Rioja wine is very slow throughout the time spent in casks.

THE FOLLOWING YEARS

Putting it simply one could say that in its first two years wine undergoes the process of spontaneous stabilisation, resulting in the formation of sediment from suspended particles of matter which prevent lustre. In the following years, once racked, the wine undergoes the true ageing process, either in barrel or in bottle. These are the processes by which aromas are purified and new ones created, the colour evolving towards a ruby red.

Of course it is not as simple as that, for the process of spontaneous stabilisation is to a large extent associated with those of ageing. A wine can create aromas typical of ageing whilst depositing small particles as sediment which still prevents lustre.

In association with this, (offering a standardised framework), the administrative standards of the Regulating Council of the Control of Origin of the Rioja dictate the periods of time to be passed in the different types of container which condition the evolution of the wine, thus exercising strict control, possibly the strictest in the world. With this common base, care taken over the choice of grapes, the great care taken in the fermentation process and care taken in their own vineyards, each bodega can make outstanding wines.

The label gives details of the commercial entity, the type of wine, the bottle capacity and the registered numbers of the bottler and Health Control. The seal or rear label guarantees that the contents have successfully passed the primary quality control of Rioja wine and that it is a product carefully controlled by the Regulating Council.

These are the minimum guarantees of the seals which are very probably simplified to:

GRAN RESERVA. Two years in cask and three in bottle.

RESERVA. One year in cask and two in bottle.

CRIANZA. One and a half years in large vats followed by one year in cask and finally half a year in bottle. In some cases this would be one year in vat, another in cask and a final year in bottle.

GUARANTEE OF ORIGIN. These are wines whose origin guarantees high quality. Although the time in bottle is not specified, the wines have been in cask sufficient time to be stable and preservable in bottle. Quality also depends on the climatic conditions prevailing during the harvest.

These are minimum guarantees offered by the bodegas. Some of the more prestigious bodegas like to go far beyond these minimums in their marketing of certain wines.

AGED WINE or "CRIANZA"
This corresponds to wines which are at least in their third year and which have been aged at least one year in oak casks.

RESERVA WINE
This corresponds to highly selected wines, which have been aged for a minimum of three years in oak casks and bottles, at least one year of which is in casks.

GRAN RESERVA
Corresponds to wines of very good harvests which have been aged for a minimum of five years in oak casks and bottles, at least two years of which are in casks.

Traditional cleaning of casks, with chains.

Automatic cask cleaning.

POLYPHENOLS

Polyphenols are the substances responsible for the colour of the grapes and therefore for the wines.

Green grapes only produce yellow polyphenols called tannins, but purple grapes also produce red polyphenols, called anthocyanins.

In time the yellow polyphenols intensify in colour and the red ones begin to disappear. A very old Rioja red owes its reddish colour to the yellow elements because of an interesting effect. This can be demonstrated with yellow cellophane paper. Looking through only one paper things are seen as yellow, but if one looks through five sheets the tone becomes reddish and with ten everything is seen as red.

Polyphenols do not only affect colour but also taste. Tannins are normally astringent. However, tannins have been noted to inter-react, joining together and losing their astringency. This happens with ageing and we have studied the oak's influence depending on whether it is American, French, old or new. The very interesting results obtained are expressed technically as polymerisation or in common language, like a smooth taste.

Here we show the results obtained from one wine in different casks during the same period of time:

Oak	Alcohol	Colour index	Taste
New American	12.35	4.24	Very smooth
Old American	12.3	3.67	Slightly harsh
New French	12.4	4.66	Smooth
Old French	12.4	4.12	Slightly harsh

These results are very interesting in that they demonstrate that new oak makes the wine smoother than old. It is true that new oak can transfer harsh elements to the wine but this is compensated by its facilitating polymerisation (smoothing) of the tannins in the wine. This happens in casks which are less than five years old.

The reaction between wine and cask is complex in its effect on the maturing of the wine, not because matter is transferred from the oak but because this activates processes in the elements in the grape which tend towards a smooth and stable wine. This is very evident in the Rioja and in Tempranillo wines.

GLOSSARY

Polyphenols. Elements found in the grape responsible for the red and yellow colours in the wine.

Anthocyanins. Red polyphenols. Only in red and rosé wines.

Tannins. Yellow polyphenols. They exist in white, red and rosé wines. They make the wine astringent.

C.I. Colour index. Relative value of the colour of a wine.

Potassium. Main natural metal component in wine, originating in the soil.

Tartaric. Main acid found in the grape which transfers to the wine.

Malic. Green grape acid which transfers to the wine. It is destroyed by the second fermentation, the wines becoming smoother.

pH. Measure of acidity in wines related to acid taste. It is an inverse measure. The greater the number the less acid the wine. For example, 3.0 pH is a very acid wine, 3.5 pH is a normal wine and 4.0 pH is a very dull wine.

The fining of Rioja wines

Since ancient times, men have felt the need to give lustre to wines, not only because this makes them more pleasing to look at but because a wine with lustre offers more subtle aromas and a finer taste.

To do this, man has resorted since antiquity to products which have the characteristics of albumen - namely, that flocculate with the alcohol, acidity and tannins in wines.

Man discovered the clarifying or fining properties of animal blood, egg white and milk. At present these means of clarification are still used, as well as others which have come to light.

The use of fresh calf's or lamb's blood is no longer authorised. But dried blood albumen is marketed and, when dissolved in water, can be used to clarify wines.

Egg albumen is still used as it has been for centuries. For every hundred litres of wine the whites of two eggs are used, whisked with a soup-spoon of common salt and added to the wine.

Milk is no longer used as such but its albumen (casein) is marketed in powder form for the fining of wines.

Each one of these clarificants performs in a specific medium:

for white wines . . . . casein
for red wines . . . . egg white
for rosé wines . . . . blood albumen

After these, other clarificants appeared, such as marrowbone jelly which is marketed in powder form and applied in the proportion of eight grammes per hundred litres of red wines.

In recent years very efficient mineral clarificants have begun to be used. One of these is a clay discovered in Fort Benton, U.S.A., appropriately named bentonite. In water, this clay forms a pasty mass similar to flour paste which flocculates with the wine and clarifies it.

More recently excellent results have been achieved in white wines by a combination of jelly and silicon dioxide.

Mineral clarificants are not new in the fining of wines. For centuries, products from deposits have been used, as is the case of the earth of Lebrija and Pozaldez.

Fining wine is carried out by adding the clarificant and stirring the wine to achieve a good mix. Two hours later, the clarificant will have flocculated, trapping the particles in suspension. For the next two days the floccules "get fat" before they finally precipitate. After ten days the clarificant with the trapped particles lies at the bottom of the vat/cask. However, it is necessary to wait a further four or five days for the sediment to settle completely so that the least amount wine is lost when this sediment is separated and removed. To do this, the clean wine is racked carefully.

In the Rioja, young red wines have traditionally been fined with jelly. Years later, in the same cask, two egg whites are used for each hectolitre and the clean wine is bottled by separating it in the same cask through the use of a stopper (a "falsete") situated above the bottom of the cask.

DISEASES IN RIOJA WINES

When considering alterations or diseases in wine from the Rioja, one has to bear in mind that by nature it is a product which is hostile to air, capable of taking this hostility to harmful extremes. Technically speaking it can become so reductive that it can spoil for this same reason.

There are certain broad chemical alterations and others which are microbiological. However, the typical deterioration in all wines by iron scarcely occurs in the Rioja. Nor does the classical microbial deterioration which causes souring. The deterioration of Rioja wine is more subtle and occasionally undefinable, but never coarse, which is necessarily the case bearing in mind that it is classified as a fine wine. This is due to the use of Tempranillo grapes, giving the wine very stable colour and lustre.

With healthy grapes there may appear, in some traditional processes, a taste of "sulphide". It is an unpleasant smell, but a consequent of a scientifically perfect fermentation. It is easily corrected by means of racking, and thus airing. It only occurs in young wines.

If the grapes deteriorate because of rain at the time of harvesting, certain moulds will develop which after fermentation could make the colour of the wine unstable, tending towards a brown colour. It is called "oxidasic failure". It is corrected quite simply by means of fining. However, these wines will not go on to being Reservas.

When young wines of an age of less than two winters are bottled, there may occur in the bottle a slight precipitation of granules similar to sugar, sometimes fused. These are bitartrates. They have no negative effect at all on the quality of the wine except for their appearance in bottle and merely denote the youth of the wine.

Once the wine is bottled it must be corked. This brief contact with the air temporarily changes the quality of its taste and aroma, the wine becoming insipid. After three months, the wine assimilates this brief contact with the air and offers all its splendour to the winetaster.

After years in bottle, because of slight oxidation through the cork, wine may offer a diminished resistance to air and lose its qualities of aroma and taste. It is said to have arrived at its "optimum" and to be "past its best".

These alterations are not caused by microbes.

The micro-organisms which live in the winemaking environment are moulds, bacteria and yeasts. In over five degrees of alcohol the moulds die. They do not survive in Rioja wines. What can happen is that through improper cleaning, wine residue can be found in a pipe or vat. This may lose its alcohol and grow moulds. If new wine is then poured into this container it will "kill" the mould but acquire its bad taste, something the people from the Rioja call "cano" ("white-hair") because of the original white colouring.

Yeasts carry out fermentation and then disappear from the wine after the sugar has been transformed to alcohol. In white and rosé wines, yeasts may remain for some time. If the wine is not well clarified before bottling, they could cause sediment in the bottle after a certain period of time. This yeast does not alter the wine itself but affects the lustre. If the effect on the lustre is strong the aroma and taste are spoilt.

Bacteria are the most frequent alterations of microbial origin.

In fermentation above 35 ºC the yeasts die and bacteria grows forming bittersweet or bitter tastes from the grape sugar. It is called the "manita" or mannitol disease.

In young rosé and white wines made from coarse-grained grapes such as the prohibited variety, Calagraño, due to a lack of substances in the skin, certain bacteria from "fibrous growth" appear making the wine sticky and syrupy. This alteration has an alarming appearance but is very easy to correct.

Red wines, after a long time in bottle, may suffer from a bacterial disease called "vuelta" ("tourne"), frequent in many wines. It is known by the French as "tourne" and by the Italians as "girato". It is a slight alteration which leaves a light sediment in the bottle and generally, though this may seem paradoxical, improves the wine, increasing its bouquet.

In the wine cellar one sometimes sees at the top of the vats/casks a white layer which the winemaker call "natas" ("skin") or "velos" ("veil"). These are yeasts that live in young wines which are not hermetically sealed. They are not of pleasant appearance but their effect on the quality of the wine, if they are not allowed to live, is very small.

All the microbes that cause alterations in wines are innocuous to man. Enologists occasionally, by way of experiment and for a better diagnostic, taste diseased wines without fear; they know that the microbes one might consume in a diseased wine will cause no harm.

THE BOTTLE

Bottles and the historical evolution of enological techniques

La Rioja, with a longitudinal extension of around 150 kilometres, produces wines which vary statistically in degrees of alcohol from 10° in the West to 16° in the East. The detailed and regular study of the evolution of these wines, which are produced in climatic regions varying from semi-humid to semi-arid, has been a most interesting and informative task. It has helped us to understand, from a historical viewpoint, the variation in consumers' tastes and the development of various wine producing regions.

We observed that usually, wines of less than 13° are spoiled by souring, whilst those of more than 13° do not become sour but mellow through the genesis of ethanal.

The alcohol content conditions the deterioration of wines exposed to air. If there is a high alcohol content, the decomposition through oxidation will only result in mellowing.

But if there is a low alcohol content, this process of oxidation continues until souring. It is well known that a mellow wine can still be considered wine, but not so a sour wine. Taking these considerations into account, we have been able to outline a history of enology which easily explains the evolution and importance of the bottle.

There is a great deal of historical data which tells us that the most appreciated wines in Hellenic or Roman times were precisely those of the Mediterranean area, because their alcohol content of over 13° allowed for slow transportation in amphoras, wineskins and "pitacos" without hermetic seals. Northern wines, with less alcohol, were for local consumption because they would go sour before the following summer.

In the 17th century the glass bottle came into use, allowing for a hermetic seal. It was also noted that by burning sulphur, wine did not go sour in the barrels used for maritime transport. These two elements, the bottle and SO_2, changed the historical course of taste and commerce in wine. It was now possible to protect wines of less than 13° from contact with air through a hermetic seal or by blocking with SO_2 the oxygen dissolved in the wine. From that time on, wines with a moderate degree of alcohol could be transported and no longer had their market limited by time and distance. Indeed, they are now perhaps the wines with a greater number of quality regions, whilst southern wines no longer have a monopoly over quality. The bottle is largely responsible as the unit of preservation, transport and consumption. However, the bottle has not only meant a change in taste and commerce, but also it has potentiated the unit value of wines from vines that can produce up to 15 metric tons of grapes per hectare, whilst Southern vines may only produce 3 metric tons per hectare with far inferior unit values. A mellow and strongly alcoholic taste has been surpassed by fresh, delicate, subtle and fruity tastes. None of this would have been possible without the bottle.

The commitment between the bottle and the enologist

Many of the customs used in the art of winemaking originated from technical necessities which, in time, have been converted into tradition and prestige. In this sense, we understand that ageing wine, rather than with chronological intentions, was undertaken in order to stabilise it. Wine began to be kept in vats, casks and barrels in order to achieve the spontaneous separation of vegetable, microbial and crystalline matter before being bottled in a clean state. Later, it was associated with some event within the family. The wine from a specific year's harvest or bottling was kept for a special occasion.

The enological industry took these habits and transformed them into a commercial activity, creating a big business dedicated to aged wine contrasting to, and sometimes in dispute with, young wines or those of a recent harvest.

Once this point had been reached, the enologist acted in favour of stabilising the wine, preserving it in the cellar under specific control for a more or less prolonged period of time in order to ship it at a later date.

The events which took place in the world economy after 1974, specifically regarding the rhetorical figure of "the price of money", obliged those responsible for the economies of wine cellars to consider the cost of capital invested in ageing wine. Many of them opted for shipping young wines to the home and export markets. But others did not wish to do this without a prestigious stock of old wines, the most famous feature of winemaking.

Even regulations like those of the Rioja, which take ageing into account in cask as well as bottle, have obliged Rioja wine cellars to store enormous quantities of bottled wine.

This means a greater commitment to bottled wine by the enologist. Generally speaking, he used to control wine in the cellar before it was consigned to the consumer. Now, at a time when the businessman's aim is to sell "future", he finds himself increasingly having to guarantee, for longer periods, a wine which is actually under his control for less time.

All of which necessitates more preparation, better equipment, more exact knowledge of the processes undergone by all kinds of wine in bottle and a precise knowledge of the climate and quality of the grapes.

At present (1990) in the Rioja only some 20% of the wines are sold on the market as Reserva and Gran Reserva. However, commercial strategies vary greatly and the tendency in some cases is towards wine which has been bottled for a long time.

Illumination and the colour of the glass used for the bottle

Although in normal storage bottled wine is kept in semi-darkness, it will inevitably be subjected to illumination which, depending on the colour of the glass, may have some effect on the stability of the wine.

For the ageing of red wine strongly-coloured bottles, verging on opaque, chromatic models no longer fashionable, are more convenient than those with green or bluish-green tones and this is evident in the taste and aromas of aged wine.

In Champagne and also in still white wines the defect known as "goût de lumière" is presumed to be due to the photochemical participation of oxygen and the reoxidising "in situ" of riboflavin. Therefore, packing which guarantees protection from solar and fluorescent light is recommended. We may deduce from the intervention of riboflavin a potentially negative effect on wines which are kept a long time on sedimented yeast.

We have investigated two experiences. One is that of white wines bottled in colourless bottles with monochromatic illumination and the other is of wines bottled in different coloured glass. Special attention was given to the microbial control:

Wine	Bottle	Light	Colour after one month	Microbes
Control	colourless	atmospheric	0.11	37
a	colourless	blue	0.16	4
b	colourless	yellow	0.17	5
c	colourless	green	0.14	18
d	colourless	red	0.14	34
In darkness			0.15	28

Tasting gave the best result to the yellow bottle. The variation in oxidation values was considerable in darkness and with green light.

The test was carried out on an unlabelled horizontal bottle.

The other study was carried out on different coloured bottles.

The results for red wine preserved in different toned bottles was as follows:

Bottle	Light received	Taste
Yellow-green	1,800 L/m^2	Acceptable
Blue-green	700 L/m^2	Acceptable
Yellow-black	160 L/m^2	Pleasant

This test on white wine gave the following results:

Bottle	Light received	Taste
Colourless	4,600 L/m^2	Oxidised
Pale green	3,500 L/m^2	Maderized
Amber I	1,450 L/m^2	Pleasant
Amber II	1,400 L/m^2	Pleasant
Yellow-green	3,350 L/m^2	Slight oxidation
Yellow-green	1,850 L/m^2	Pleasant
Blue-green	700 L/m^2	Pleasant
Black amber	60 L/m^2	Pleasant

Through these studies we cannot define a qualitative influence of light, but we can define a quantitative influence. The greater the amount of light received, the more notable the oxidation phenomena detected by winetasting and the observation of increased colour.

Rhine, Bordeaux and Burgundy bottles.

EVOLUTION OF WINE
IN THE BOTTLE

Esterifications of the wine in bottle

As wine is a hydroalcoholic acid solution, the formation of esters is normal. Acids (fundamentally) intervene in the esterification of wine. Ester is a combination of alcohol and acid.

Esterification reactions are very slow processes limited by reserved saponifications.

The phenomena of esterification has been held greatly responsible for the bouquet of wine. In our investigation of bottled Spanish wines, we have come to believe that, rather than being fundamental to quality, they can be considered in a positive sense as the fruit of a contained process of little importance in old wine. However they also have a notable incidence in negative processes. We have begun to attribute more responsibility to ethanol for the rancid taste acquired in ageing than to the inevitable common base of polyphenolic substances.

Esterification in the bottle is conditioned by acidity values and the nature of the acid, tartaric and acetic acid being predominant in the process. It is not so much the case with other acids. Actually, ethyl acetate is the dominant ester in numerous wines. It is held more responsible for the souring characteristic than acetic acid (vinegar) itself and its perception threshold is estimated at being between 180 and 200 mg/l.

In bottled red wines of the Rioja, the threshold in our tests of addition of ethyl acetate to the content determined by analysis is:

	Threshold value
Red wine of crushed grape	170 mg/l.
Red wine with CO_2 maceration	195 mg/l.

Ethyl acetate is basically a sign of degradation in quality and, as with volatile acidity, enologists are interested in achieving low values for consumption, around 100 mg./l. For this reason, it is convenient to know the circumstances which cause high or low levels of ethyl acetate.

On bottling, Rioja wines have levels between 60 and 100 mg/l. The highest levels occur in young wines under 12 months.

Later, in bottle, the level rises very slowly, depending on previous cleanliness during fermentation and in cask.

Sulphates in bottled wine

For organic purposes, we have studied the level of sulphates contained in bottled wine. They originate in the grape and increase with ageing.

A study of various wines which had been kept in bottle for different periods of time offered the following results:

Time in the bottle	Sulphates (g/l.)
15-20 years	1.7-2.1
10-15 years	0.7-1.1
5-10 years	0.6-1.0
2- 5 years	0.5-0.9
0- 2 years	0.4-0.9

It is easy to appreciate that evolution in bottle tends to increase the level of sulphates in the wine. But the samples studied show a considerable rate of increase after ten years.

Following the progress of just one product and controlling bottles at different times gave the following results:

Sample	Sulphates (g/l.)
Day of bottling	0.52
After one year	0.60
After two years	0.73
After three years	0.90

The increase is contained and is one more symptom of the complex ageing processes in bottles that undergo very slow oxidation.

Aromas of bottled wine

The aromas of Spanish bottled wines have not been studied individually or in groups. Our studies are based on industrial empiricism.

A unified quantity of red wine taken from a cask where it had been kept for two years was separated into smaller tempered units of stainless steel and bottled in monthly stages.

After a year, a control was carried out on the sample bottles of each bottled portion, controlling iron and initial red colour after 24 hours, and classifying the taste:

Wine	Wavelength 520	Wavelength 420	Iron	Class of aromas
Initial	1.6	1.62	2.2	Weak
After 1 month	1.48	1.54	1.7	Slight
After 2 months	1.47	1.58	1.3	Slight
After 3 months	1.43	1.63	0.9	Pleasant
After 4 months	1.38	1.66	0.6	Pleasant
After 6 months	1.41	1.64	0.4	Pleasant
After 12 months	1.40	1.63	0.6	Pleasant

In this wine, typical of the Rioja, there exists a rapid reductive process which manifests itself in the almost complete disappearance of ferric iron and the passing from a red colour to a variant. The colour decreases and returns with air contact. A parallel situation is observed in the aroma. Once the reduction point is reached, the aroma is pleasantly appreciated.

However, from the aromatic point of view, one appreciated feature is only developed in wines after one or two years in bottle. This is the reduction aroma of pleasing nuances for the Spanish subjectivity, it disappears from the glass after a few minutes.

"Viña Arana" bottle-ageing warehouse.

In this type of wine there are three phases to the tasting:
A. The initial phase of reduction in the bouquet, two minutes in the glass.
B. There follows a neutral phase of some five minutes in the glass.
C. Finally the wine gives off aromas of an oxidative nuance at the same time as that of the oak.

These three "readings" of the aromas of a wine with a long shelf life influence the winetasting experience. There frequently occurs in the A phase a "dry and harsh" aftertaste which is lost in phase B and is supplanted by another harsh nuance of oak in phase C.

Wine, in its aromatic aspect, goes through a crisis after some months in the bottle. It takes on a reduced character, expressing, very smoothly, the aromas assimilated in cask and later creating its own aromatic characteristics in the reduction process.

Compounds responsible for colour

In simple terms, we could define the subject of this chapter as the evolution of colouring matter in bottled wine. We must acknowledge that phenolic compounds and, more specifically, polyphenolic compounds, in addition to giving wine its characteristic colour, are, to a large extent, responsible for the aroma and taste.

Below, we offer a brief description of the evolution of wine from the grape to the moment it enters the bottle, assuming a normal maceration (in the case of red

wine) and ageing in 225-litre casks for one to two years. A good comprehension of this process is essential to understanding the evolution of wine in bottle, also the relationship this has with previous processes and its consequences.

Wine arrives at the bottling plant after losing a considerable amount of anthocyanins during the time in cask (depending on the age of the casks). The tannin condensation process by polymerisation has already begun.

Although technical personnel work hard applying stabilising measures to the wine which is to be bottled, fortunately, when the product is received, it is in full polyphenolic development. At most, we stabilise marginal aspects such as microbiology or crystallizations, allowing its colour to evolve naturally.

In general terms, the evolution of wine in bottle represents a continuity of the activities which take place in cask, except for the absorption of tannin from the oak. Anthocynanins continue to disappear and tannins increase, in a clearly reducing environment. The cork represents a defence against oxidation. Any deterioration of the reducing power through the cork is unusual.

Depending on the variety, there are two types of colour evolution. Accordingly, we have established that wine ages in two different ways in bottle:

Type I. Rapid change. Prototype: Garnacha (Grenache).
Type II. Slow change and then stable. Prototype: Tempranillo.

This means that the colour of Garnacha ages very early and deteriorates very quickly.

In contrast Tempranillo ages very slowly, but later remains matured and stable for a long period of time.

This is due to the different evolution, or speed with which the red colour decreases and the yellow colour increases. Therefore, the colouring process which is present in cask, continues in bottle, but in the latter case, the process is much slower.

The reduction which is observed in the red colour is due to the destruction of anthocyanins. The yellow colour increases due to the joining of molecules, or polymerisation.

The development of anthocyanins (decreasing) and polymerisation (increasing) is sensitive to atmospheric temperatures. At less than 5° C, the process stops, it reaches its optimum level at around 30° C. However in practice, if there is a temperature variation during the conservation of bottles, not only does temperature have a bearing on its development, but it also provokes changes in volume (in temperature variations of more than 8° C). This means an interaction between the mass of wine and the mass of cork which could cause an imbalance in the normal reducing level. A bottle kept at 20° C deteriorates quicker than at 10° C.

The empty space between the cork and wine is necessary in order to absorb moderate thermal changes. An excessive space increases the oxidation of the wine in bottle, but an absence of this air space decreases the temperature changes causing regurgitations. This spoils the wine, entering the cork and then affecting the bottle.

Today, wine is usually bottled without air, in an inert atmosphere of nitrogen and carbon dioxide gas.

Alcohol in the bottle

When wines are aged for a long time in bottle, they seem to lose some alcohol through the cork, but do not deteriorate for this reason.

It is estimated that when stored in cellars with a 49-mm cork, a bottle placed in the horizontal position loses 1% of alcohol in 25 years, i.e., one degree; but this degree is lost as of the 15th year. For this reason, corks are changed in the case of wines which remain for more than 15 years in bottles.

Sediments in the bottle

Over the years, enological techniques have advanced greatly. In previous times wine was cloudy when bottled, maintaining a biological struggle between yeast and bacteria thus preventing the wine from becoming vinegary. Today, by extracting the microbian or crystalline agents of instability, it is possible to bottle wines free from the risk of turbidity and refermentations but with the natural activity of colouring matter. We can bottle stable wines without stopping the evolutionary process in bottle. Therefore, there is no technological justification for sediments of bacteria or wine-colouring matter.

The position of the bottle

In simple terms, it is recognised that the bottle must remain in a horizontal position so that the wine can dampen the cork and in this way, prevent it from becoming spoiled due to a lack of dampness.

Through several different studies of the relationship between wine and corks, we have determined that wine has a harmful effect on the cork. Different tests showed that polyphenolic matter present in wine attacks the cork and the degree of alcohol has a direct influence on the penetration of the cork mass by the wine. However, the most surprising results were obtained by the empirical testing of wines which were kept for ten years in bottle, some horizontal and others vertical. The corks extracted from horizontal bottles were of high density and low elasticity; while those of vertical bottles kept their initial density and were of greater elasticity. This means that wine can deteriorate the cork once in bottle. We are not so bold as to make recommendations against storing in the horizontal position, but this is under review.

The open bottle

On some occasions, doubts arise concerning the advisability of opening a bottle and drinking the wine immediately, or, of allowing some time to elapse between these two events.

The data we have accumulated generally advises that wine be consumed very quickly, soon after the cork is removed from the bottle. However, we cannot advise against consuming wine after a degree of contact with air. After the bottle has been opened, wine undergoes three changes:

  I. An immediate change in which reduction can be observed.
 II. Later, there is a time of neutral aromas. After some hours there is another evolution of the flavour.
III. The appearance of lively aromas with a certain degree of oxidation.

The amount of time which elapses from phase I to phase III depends on the iron content. 24 hours for wines open to the air with total iron of more than 8 mg/l, and slower if the iron content is lower.

In general terms, Rioja wine does not require breathing before consumption.

←
"Gran Reserva 904" ageing tunnel.

CORKING

The weak point in the system used to seal the bottle is the cork; a natural product which adds to the final appearance of the bottle and its efficiency.

Corking depends on:

The fit in the bottle neck.
The corking device clamp.
The quality and dimensions of the cork.

The basic factor is the quality of the cork. It is assumed that the other factors are of minimum importance due to the fact that:

Today, bottling plants pay attention to the compression of the cork so as not to leave folds on the surface as was the case with the clamps of old corking devices.

The moulds used by bottle manufacturers now tend to control the diameter of the neck of the bottle where the cork is housed so that it is perfectly compressed in all bottles.

It should be said that many years ago there may have been an appreciable variation in the internal diameter of the necks of bottles, causing the unsatisfactory fit of some corks.

However the most important question is the quality of the cork.

CORKS
Biological aspects. Duration and evolution of corks

When we wish to extend the duration of the agreeable taste of a wine we tend to consider that the only variable factor is the wine, and that the glass and cork are inert. However we observe that glass is the only inert element; not the cork, which is subject to attack by moths and moulds. Nevertheless, from the enological point of view, we are interested in determining whether cork, apart from its use in bottling, has permanent characteristics or whether it evolves in any way from the moment it is taken from the cork oak.

To do this, we have studied cork bark or sheets of cork, submitted to chemical attack, drying or simple ageing.

The attached chart shows the dimensions studied:

a) Direction of the particles.
b) Direction of the rings.
c) Height or length of the sheet.

In normal corks these dimensions mean:

a and b, top and bottom cork diameters.

c, height of the cork.

Red wine cork, new cork and white wine cork.

Manual corking of Gran Reserva
"Marqués de Haro".

146

Variation in sheet dimensions			
	a	**b**	**c**
40-60% atmospheric humidity for six months	−1.3%	−3.7%	−1.8%
Drying at 100 ºC for 24 hours	−0.6%	−4.3%	−1.1%
In water for one month	+0.2%	+1.3%	+1.2%
In 1% aqueous alcoholic solution	+1.8%	+2.4%	+1.8%
In 1% tartaric solution	+2.3%	+1.7%	+1.8%

These results demonstrate that the dimensions of corks evolve differently with respect to wine and the atmosphere: their oscillation being greater in the annular direction of the sheet. This creates a discrepancy between cork diameters from the moment they are cut, depending on:

The age, from the moment when the cork is cut.

The dryness which has been endured.

The damaging effects of dampness.

For this reason, we make reference in this study to the concept of "different diameters" in corks as a difference of measurements in the direction of its particles and perpendicular.

To conclude, the dimensions of corks evolve naturally and in the form of an annular contraction of the sheet. It can be said that:

"Corks come from a living element which evolves in the original tangential direction. The quality of the cork over a long period of time depends, especially in the case of the first layer of bark, on the conditions which bring forward or delay this contraction".

Physical aspects

Corks have variable densities.

The densities recorded cover a wide range from 0.1 to 0.23.

From a practical point of view, the lowest densities usually correspond to bigger cells and these corks tend:

a) To fall into the bottle when the corkscrew is introduced.

b) To push out during hot spells or when bottles are filled without an air space.

c) To stay fast even when the corkscrew passes right through.

The higher density of some corks is due to a more compact structure or due to a heterogeneous softer part, compensated by cracks with woody walls. The defect associated with high-density corks is, in principle, that they crack on being extracted.

The measurements we have made of elasticity demonstrate that this is the result of variations in density.

Therefore, in practice, there is a wide variety of commercially-available corks, from the density point of view, and this includes, in addition to the basic group of medium density corks, very light or very heavy corks.

It is considered that a quality methodology for corking can be established, based on this study of cork density; it consists of:

A) Visual observation (of 50 corks).

B) Weighing of 50 corks (those submitted to observation beforehand).

Visually, corks can be eliminated in accordance with quality requirements by observing abnormal instances of pores, cracked veins, deformations, the greenish ring of moulds or the obstruction of pores.

Based on weighing the evaluation process will afterwards narrow the range of selection for the more demanding qualities, trimming the "wings of the Gauss curve".

All meshes are fastened manually.

We recommend, for three different quality levels and for corks of 49 mm, the following characteristics for long-term conservation:

	Min. Density	Max. Density	Weight range
A) The most demanding	0.15	0.19	3.3-4.2
B) Intermediate	0.14	0.20	3.1-4.4
C) Low*	0.13	0.21	2.9-4.7

* In this case a visually rejectable cork can be admitted.

Microbian aspects

Studies we have carried out on Rioja Reserva wines with bottling periods ranging from six months to thirty-two years, have shown that:

Moulds are the natural inhabitants of corks.

During ageing in bottles placed horizontally, wine penetrates the entire length of the cork, neutralising a large part of the moulds in the interior.

Paradoxically, corks of very old wines reveal large growths of moulds but these are situated on the outside of the cork.

The dominant types of moulds in long-life corks are Aspergillus and Penicillium.

From the microbian point of view, moulds are already present in corks available for bottling.

Moulds persist and are maintained in all corks. However, the capacity of these moulds to reproduce themselves in an appropriate environment does not imply that the cork can transfer taste to the mould; this would occur in the case of exaggerated levels of dampness in corks.

The presence of yeasts and bacteria in commercial corks is not frequent, but they can be seen in the veins of low-quality corks filled with cork shavings and mastics.

From the point of view of sterile bottling, we have determined that moulds do not constitute a risk but, considering the low numbers of yeasts and the assumption that corks are important transmitters of yeasts, the sampling of sacks of corks is recommended.

In addition to these microscopic agents, corks can be attacked by moths if the bottle is not capped and if humidity is very low.

Chemical aspects. The harmful effect of wine on the cork.

Although wine is the substance to be conserved, the behaviour of the cork as a seal does not only depend on its evolution in time, in accordance with the atmosphere; but also on the characteristics of the wine in the bottle which can affect the condition of the cork during long-term ageing.

For this study we have investigated several corks of the highest quality available on the market in order to consider their behaviour in the presence of several components of wine.

I) BEHAVIOUR IN THE PRESENCE OF TANNIN

Corks made by three manufacturers were submitted to a hydroalcohol bath at 10° at a pH of 3.2; in some cases with tannin at 1 g/l, with the following results:

Cork	Means	Drained weight	Dry weight	Diameter difference
I	without treatment	+45.0%	−5.6%	−0.15%
I	with tannin	+51.0%	−4.1%	−0.15%
II	without treatment	+37.5%	−6.3%	−0.25%
II	with tannin	+42.9%	−7.45%	−0.34%
III	without treatment	+29.6%	−8.4%	−0.33%
III	with tannin	+45.7%	−8.75%	−0.37%

Tannin appears to accelerate the contraction of the diameter of corks and the impregnation of dampness.

II. BEHAVIOUR IN THE PRESENCE OF ALCOHOL

Tests carried out were made with vacuum-evaporated white wine and with alcohol made up at varying degrees. The corks remained immersed in the wine for one month.

Degree of the liquid	Diameter difference	Drained weight
6°	0.06	+7.0%
12.5°	0.1	+9.8%
22°	0.14	+20.8%

It is shown that the degree of alcohol is important in the diffusion of liquid inside the cork although it does not appear to have a considerable effect on changes in diameter.

III) INFLUENCE OF THE POSITION OF BOTTLES.

We have studied a group of bottles of red wine from the same bottling operation. Some having remained in a horizontal position and others vertical, with an extremely variable atmosphere ranging from -10ºC to +40ºC and humidity from 30% to 98%.

The horizontal group: weight from 4.03 to 4.44 g and diameters ranging within 10 days from 20.5 mm outside to 20.2 mm on the inner surface, dampened by the wine.

The vertical group (dry): weight from 3.5 to 3.7 g, the average dimensions within 10 days being 20.8 mm on the outside and 21.3 mm inside (next to the wine).

IV) INFLUENCE OF THE GRAPE VARIETY.

We have studied the quality and evolution of the wine/cork relationship for the Cabernet and Tempranillo varieties with at least four years of storage in bottle and with four different types of cork:

A) Red Cabernet wine.

Type of cork	External diameter	Internal diameter
a	20.2 mm	20.5 mm
b	20.2 mm	19.8 mm
c	20.6 mm	20.6 mm
d	19.5 mm	20.2 mm

All these corks were heavily stained.

B) Tempranillo red.

Type of cork	External diameter	Internal diameter
a	21.8 mm	23.0 mm
b	22.2 mm	22.2 mm
c	21.2 mm	22.3 mm
d	21.2 mm	22.2 mm

Lightly stained corks.

These results are not conclusive but seem to show that wine from the different grape varieties has a widely ranging effect on the cork during long periods in bottle. In the case of some types of wine, corks contract readily inside when they are in contact with wine, as is shown by the diameter of corks extracted from bottles of old wines.

The harmful effect of corks on wine.

The taste of the cork.
Some corks give a disagreeable taste to wine. This subject is controversial and is extremely important for old wine or wine which must remain a long time in bottle.

Rigault, Issanchou, Sarris and Langlois determined that the intrinsic "cork taste" which some wines have is due to 2-4-6 trichloroanisole (2-4-6 TCA). Nevertheless, some authors such as Riboullet attribute this taste specifically to cork moulds; Wurdig to moulds in the bodega and the use of pentachlorophenol as a disinfectant for wood. Maujean, Millery and Lemarseguier also attribute this to 2-4-6 TCA and to the use of chlorated compounds as a disinfectant for corks.

We attribute certain responsibility to the wine for this strange taste. In tests using wines of different origin and the same corks, some acquire a disagreeable taste and others do not. This occurs with wines from a grape with oxidative polyphenols, such as Garnacha, which readily acquire this disagreeable taste. Therefore, although no precise evidence is available, we understand that the cork taste comes from the cork but is especially noticeable in some wines.

We have also observed that the cork taste is more noticeable in wines with a low pH.

After studying a series of corks, the taste of which could be noticed in the wine and comparing these with others which did not, we could not find any difference, either in quality or in quantity, of the population of microbes.

CONSERVATION IN BOTTLES

Only new bottles are used; they are washed before bottling.

The weak point in a bottle of Rioja wine is the cork. The cork is a living element which after being taken from the cork oak, continues to age slowly. This implies very slow contraction which may, in the long term, cause deformation in the diameter of the cork.

Corks follow the same process in the bottle. At the end of ten or twenty years it loses its sealing powers. At the end of more than 25 years, this seal may be less than perfect, allowing air to enter and even permitting wine to escape.Then, the wine becomes vinegary and cloudy.

This process is very slow and should not alarm consumers of Rioja wines. Wineries control the quality of corks closely and use the most expensive types available. Today, Gran Reserva wines are bottled with corks which are four times more expensive than those used for wines bottled in the year following the vintage.

Due to reasons which are easy to understand, the consumer wants his or her wine to retain its taste for a long time so the bottle must be in good condition.

A high conservation temperature of over 20º C means:

— The expansion of wine and loss through the cork.
— The possible ejection of the cork.
— The premature ageing of the cork.
— The acceleration of the chemical processes in wine, which shorten its life.

A temperature which is too low, i.e., below 5º C, makes all the above points difficult, but facilitates the coupling of polyphenols, which are responsible for colour, producing sediment in the wine and accentuating the instability of its clarity.

Cyclical temperature variation is least beneficial. This can occur when the bottle is in the window of an establishment, heating up during the day and becoming cool at night. This causes thermal changes bringing about all the above-mentioned disadvantages, plus periodic regurgitation of the wine through the cork, with the incorporation of moulds and substances from the cap and exterior.

Light always causes wine to oxidise, and Rioja wine, as in the case of other famous Appellations, is the enemy of oxidation.

It is difficult to talk about the position of bottles. Contrary to everything which has been said about the advantage of the wine dampening the cork so that it does not become dry, we have seen that wine also attacks the cork, making it lose its elasticity. This process is very slow, but it has been demonstrated that bottles which are kept in a vertical position maintain their quality for a long period of time, better than in those which are placed horizontally.

Nevertheless, although the above-mentioned results are accurate and true, we still do not have enough experience in the subject to recommend that a bottle of Rioja wine be kept in a vertical position.

To summarise, we can say that bottles of Rioja should be kept under the following conditions:

- Moderate temperature, between 9 and 12° C.
- Atmospheric humidity above 70%.
- Placed horizontally (until proved otherwise).
- Absence of light.
- Absence of smells.
- Absence of wood containing moths.

The questions which consumers often ask can be answered simply:

- **Does wine improve in the bottle?** Bottled wine continues a process which is conditioned by the personality of the vintage and the variety of grape. We can say that this process does, in synthesis, improve the quality of the wine.
- **How long can wine remain in the bottle?** The life of the wine in bottle depends on its weakest point, the cork, and the conditions under which the bottle is stored. Without light and at a low constant temperature, of about 5° C, wine can remain in bottle in good condition for dozens of years.
- **Once a wine has been bottled, how long must it remain in the bottle before being consumed?** The standards set by the Regulating Council are very strict in this respect and stipulate very long periods in bottle. Our studies show that in three months wine recovers from the oxidative impact of the bottling operation. As of that moment, wine continues to mature and evolve slowly in bottle, sometimes for many years.

156

CAPSULES AND LABELS

The capsules which cover the mouth of the bottle are made from various materials such as plastic, aluminium or tinned lead. Rioja wines usually used tinned lead sheet for capsules, taking advantage of the malleable nature of the lead and the inertia of the tin. It is a made like "sandwich" material with two layers of tin which cover the lead on each side. Now other "sandwich" material lead free is used.

Sometimes the capsules are perforated to allow the cork to breathe. This reasoning is not completely sound, as unperforated caps have been used for years, with no apparent problems.

Using wax is an age-old practice. It was believed to be a perfect sealing process for the cork. However, in practice the wax peeled away and was useless as a result of lack of flexibility and adhesion in damp areas. Paraffin has also been used; but it is the capsule that offers the advantage of being both a flexible and adjustable seal, avoiding the need to break wax or paraffin when serving at table.

The bottle is defined by the name of the brand being stated on the label. As a guarantee, the cork and capsule also name the bodega. The back label indicates the Control of the Rioja and the front label the bodega and the bottler and sanitary registration number.

The label, the bodega's own personalised "flag", shows the brand name, type of wine, vintage, the place where the wine is bottled and the Control of Origin, in addition to information on volume, alcohol content, the Control of Origin seal of the Rioja Regulating Council, also included are the registration number of the bottling warehouse, and the Health Authority registration number.

The bodega has the option of using a neck label or its own back label on the bottle, provided that the name or seal of the Regulating Council also appears on the rear label.

If we compare Rioja labels with those used for Bordeaux wines, we can see differences which have no value in themselves, but are simply different ways of presenting the wines.

Bordeaux labels tend to use "colder" colours than Rioja, where ochre or parchment colours are still considered important. We also tend to use heraldic symbols and coats of arms more frequently, with fewer outside views of the bodega. As far as general vineyard views are concerned, these are used as much on Bordeaux as on Rioja labels.

A suitable reason for criticism would be the Rioja wines, which setting out to be young and fresh (even in the Gran Reserva, which are far from rancid and maderized in taste) tended to over-use parchment or leathery colours on their labels, these always have associations of being "old but not fresh".

WINETASTING AND ANALYSES

APPRECIATION OF COLOUR AND BRILLIANCE.

White, rosé and red.

Before we can begin to talk of winetasting, the basic conditions for tasting must be established. The same type of wine tasted in different glasses appears to be different wine.

For this reason, the winetasting glass has been standardised and has become an instrument with a certain degree of precision, allowing a uniform set of criteria to be established.

The standardised tasting glass (AFNOR) offers the best conditions for tasting the majority of fine table wines, in colour, brilliance, aroma and taste. A specific model is advisable in the case of special wines. It is made of glass, with a minimum of 26% lead, melted with silver sand at 1,500° C. It is blown by mouth, providing it with delicacy and lightness. It has a density of 2.4, while normal glasses have only 2.0.

It is, in short, an intermediate glass between the "caña" of Jerez and the rounded brandy glass.

For tasting, it is filled to a third of its capacity.

The colour and brilliance of the wine can be seen clearly.

Brilliance means the absence of suspended matter and from this point of view a wine can be classed as being cloudy, turbid, "jaro" (a typical Rioja expression), clean, bright or very bright.

Brilliance is obtained by allowing the wine to age in cask in the bodega, followed by clarification. Nevertheless, human eyes do not have sufficient capacity to detect brilliance; a wine with up to a thousand microbes per cubic centimetre can appear bright. Consequently, wines leave the bodega with an adequate level of brightness (from the technical point of view), obtained with clarifiers (gelatine or egg white) which allow the brightness to be maintained for years.

The colour of wine is a blend of the natural colouring which is present in grapes. This blend gives rise to a certain capacity of colour or intensity and a quality or tone.

Grape colouring is basically yellow and is present in the skin and pulp. Red grapes also have red colouring in the skin. The red colouring is called anthocyanin and the yellow, tannin. Therefore, a white wine is yellow; due to the fact that it comes only from white grapes and only has tannins. On the other hand, rosés or red wines have, in addition to the tannin which gives it a yellow colour, a small amount of red in the case of rosé, or a large amount in the case of reds.

With the passing of time, the red colour of the anthocyanin begins to disappear while the tannins oxidise slowly and increase in colour. In this way, a young white wine is straw-coloured and when old, is golden in colour. While a young rosé is bright pink, when old it has a colour similar to "onion skin". A red wine is purple when young and ruby-red when old; it has a "leather-like" colour when very old.

Burgundy and Bordeaux glasses and the
official tasting glass of the Rioja.

In reality this is not so simple, although there is some truth in this idea. We admit that it is not so simple because maceration plays an important role. It is possible to soak the skins or not, increasing or decreasing the time. All this might lead one to think that red grapes could be used to make white, rosé or red wine.

In the Rioja, grapes have very specific uses, each grape being used to make the wine it is most suited for.

Viura	White
Garnacha	Rosé
Tempranillo	Red

This being the case it could be understood that there is a variation between quantity and quality of colour. For example, in a glass, two wines can have the same amount of apparent colour, but studied closely one could be pure red and the other have a tendency towards a "leather-like" colour.

The explanation of the concept of white, rosé, "claret" and red also fits in with this general idea. A white wine is fermented without skins contrary to a red wine which is fermented with skins until the end, i.e., until it becomes wine. Rosé falls between these two concepts and is fermented without skins but the must comes from a mixture of red and white grapes. A similar case is that of "claret" (today in disuse), which is the fermentation of the red grape on the skins until the wine is only half processed.

The appreciation of colour in a glass requires very specific conditions of light and atmosphere.

Lighting is conditioned by the tradition of using a candle. In this sense, similar types of lighting, such as sun light or lamps with or without halogen filaments can be used. A high reproductivity is advisable; this is difficult to obtain with high or low pressure discharge lamps. Nevertheless, the range of fluorescent lamps is so wide that they can be eliminated systematically. There are models with very high reproductivity, such as TLD-93 and 95. These concepts refer to the quality of illumination. Regarding quality, a minimum amount of 700 Lux for whites, 1,000 for rosés, 1,500 for old red wines and 4,000 for young reds.

The environment should have a high reflective value of over 65; this is given in white, at the most with a blue-violet tendency, but not yellow.

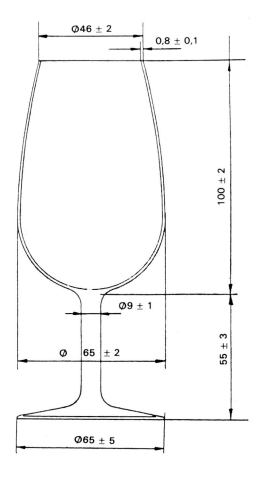

AFNOR standardised glass (one type is winetasting 2772 "Spanish Bohemia"). Useful for appreciating colour of reds and rosés although not so much for whites. However, it is useful for observing brightness and appreciating aromas in all types of wines. (Dimensions in millimetres).

APPRECIATION OF AROMAS

The substances which give rise to the aromatic sensations of wines are extremely diversified and numerous. Perhaps some five hundred are known today. In the future, with the advances made in analytical methods, there may be many more.

According to their nature they can be grouped into:

Alcohols
Acids
Ethers
Carbonylic compounds
Amines
Terpene hydrocarbons
Carotenes

Each compound shows its smell according to:

Concentration
Boiling point
Peculiarity

The appreciation of aroma is also known as:

Appreciation of smell
Appreciation of aromas

The name which best responds to this activity is the "appreciation of aromas".

It is generally recognised that once the cork has been removed from the bottle, the wine should be submitted to a visual appreciation: brightness and colour. Afterwards, aroma and finally, the palate. In fact, tasting should begin with the appreciation of the aromas, for the simple reason that if there are fleeting aromas, be they good or bad, these could be lost if we take time making a visual appreciation of the wine.

Sensitivity to smell lies in the upper part of the nasal passages where volatile vapours arrive by two routes.

1. Direct, through the nose, when the wine is smelled beneath it.

2. Retronasal, or indirect, when the wine evaporates in the mouth cavity and its aroma passes behind the palate into the nasal passage.

The appreciation of aromas is a complex process.

The standard glass is useful for appreciating the aroma of wine. An open, goblet-type glass would not be appropriate.

The temperature of the wine has a great deal of influence on the appreciation of the aromas. Low temperatures attenuate the aromas and high temperatures develop the retronasal aromatic pressure in excess (not pleasant), and makes them seem sickly sweet. For this reason, there is a temperature limit for the appreciation of aromas which is estimated at 15-16° C maximum, giving aroma via the retronasal duct of 25-26° C. Above these temperatures the wine would not be pleasant to drink.

Time is equally important for the appreciation of aromas. The aroma of wine which is poured into a glass immediately after opening the bottle develops in three stages:

1. For three minutes it shows the bouquet which is developed during the time in bottle.

2. Following this, there are five minutes of neutral aroma.

3. Finally, it reveals an aroma of oak from the casks.

It should be easy now to recognise primary, secondary aromas, etc. as types of aromas. Gradually, new effects, components and reasons for taste are discovered. Their origin is very complex.

Aromas may come from:

GRAPES	Skin, and in Malvasia and Muscat, the pulp.
THE PRE-FERMENTATION PROCESSES	Transport Sulphites Pressing Debourbage
FERMENTATION	Vigorous Malolactic Carbonic maceration
TECHNOLOGY	Fining Filtration Racking, etc.
AGEING	Reduction process Oak The effects on the wine when the cork seals the bottle Time in bottle.

APPRECIATION OF TASTE

The taste of wine is understood as being both flavour and "palate". It is a very complex concept which depends on several factors.

The main factors which make up flavour are:

The acids present in wine
Alcohol
Polyphenols (red and yellow colourings of the grape)
Carbonic gas

Although it is generally accepted that sensitivity for sweet, bitter, acid and salty tastes are centred on the tongue, in winetasting, sensations are much more complex. After swallowing, impressions remain on the tongue, palate, the velum of the palate, gums, inside the lips and in front of the throat (aftertaste).

The polyphenols, or colour, which exists in wine, also have a marked influence on taste. White wines can have 0.2 g/l and reds 2 g/l. The more polyphenols present, the more astringent the taste will be. This is noticeable at low temperatures. The lower the temperature of a wine, the more astringent its taste. In this way, wines with little colour, (whites and rosés) can be consumed at 10° C. In the case of reds, the temperature should not go below 15° C.

Alcohol rounds off the taste of wine, generally making it milder. If we were to remove the alcohol from the wine we would be surprised by its astringency and acidity. Glycerine contained in wines from 4 to 7 g/l also contributs to this effect.

Wine contains acids which are either derived from the grape or formed during fermentation. The following elements come from the grapes:

Tartaric acid. Responsible for "hard" acidity and ranges from 3 to 6 g/l.
Malic acid. Responsible for a "green" taste and ranges from 0 to 3 g/l.
Citric acid. Responsible for a "fresh" taste, which only exists from 0.2 to 0.4 g/l.

The following elements are derived from fermentation:

Lactic acid. Responsible for an agreeable bitter taste similar to yoghurt. From 1 to 2 g/l.
Succinic acid. Hot and agreeable acid taste. From 0.5 to 1.5 g/l.
Acetic acid. Disagreeable and causes deterioration. From 0.2 to 0.6 g/l in healthy wines.

Carbon dioxide gas exists in wines naturally. There is a lot in young wines and little in older wines. In a young wine, it is better to keep one gramme per litre of CO_2 for highlighting freshness. In December, new wines contain too much carbon dioxide gas, this is not pleasant. In summer CO_2 usually drops to half a gramme per litre which is not pleasant either. On the other hand, it is not good for old wines to contain more than 0.3 g/l.

Winetasting essentially means a method for defining aromas, appearance and taste. These are not easy to separate as they are not independent. We shall attempt to define:

First, the direct impression of aroma.
Second, visual observation; brilliance and colour.

Then on to the palate. Winetasting must be carried out:

- Keeping wine in one's mouth for five seconds produces a "hot sensation" on the tongue if it contains CO_2 or "aguja" ("petillant").
- By sucking in air, the aroma will be picked up by the nose via the retronasal passage.
  After swallowing the wine, one will immediately be left with:
  A lingering taste on the palate, tongue and gums.
  A smooth or "petillant" aftertaste at the front of the throat.

SUMMARY

Environment:

Atmospheric temperature .... 20° C ■ 1° C
Lighting .... 700 - 5,000 Lux
Winetasting glass .... AFNOR 2772
"Spanish Bohemia"
Wine temperature .... 10° C White, rosé
Wine temperature. 12° C Red. CO_2 maceration.
Wine temperature .... 15° C Red in general.
Luminous reflection 65%
Atmospheric humidity 60-80%
Chromatic yield of light ..... More than 85%

Method:

1. Immediate appreciation on opening the bottle.
2. Initial appreciation of aroma.
3. Observation of brilliance and colour.
4. The wine is drunk and kept in the mouth for five seconds to check for CO_2, noticeable in a sensation of "petillant" on the tongue.
5. Suction of air through the mouth and appreciation of aroma.
6. The wine is swallowed or expelled.
7. Immediate definition of impressions left on the palate, tongue and gums.
8. Definition of aftertaste.
9. New direct appreciation of aroma and comparison with initial impression.
   This process must be carried out with the same proportion of wine in the glass.

Assessment:

Explanation of chart.
a) Points for initial appreciation of aroma.
b) Points for brilliance.
c) Points for colour (white in yellow area and red in both)
d) Points for appreciation of aromas.
e) Points for residual taste on gums.
f) Points for residual taste on tongue.
g) Points for residual taste on palate.
h) Points for aftertaste.

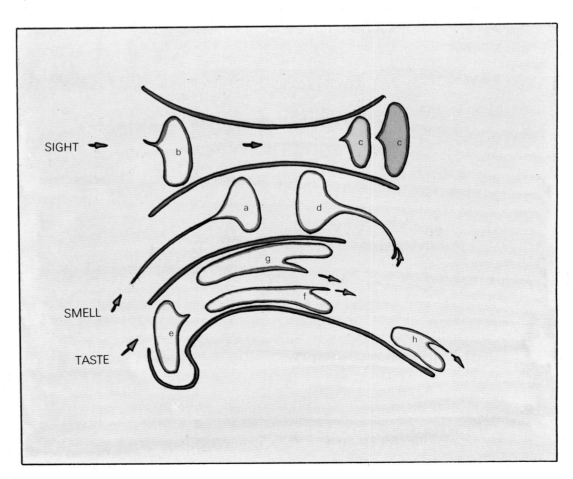

ANALYSIS

Analysis of alcohol

Wine is a moderately alcoholic drink. Alcohol in wine comes from a natural process called fermentation and is made at the expense of the sugar contained in the grape. Each 17.5 g of sugar giving one degree of alcohol, which is one per cent by volume.

The type of alcohol present in wine is ethanol or ethylic alcohol.

Rioja wines have from 10° to 14° of alcohol. Red wines are usually between 12° and 13°. White and rosé between 10° and 12°. The matter is not simple for whites and rosés. Some years ago, the Market demanded these wines have an alcohol level of 13° and that they be aged in oak. Today, this type of wine is appreciated only by a limited number of consumers. The Market demands whites and rosés with a lower alcohol level. Nevertheless, it is now possible to see a tendency back to the ageing of white wines in wood.

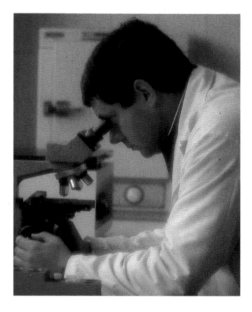

The consumer does not ask for a specific alcohol level, but for wines with "body" and long life (attained with grapes which give almost 13° of alcohol); or light, fresh whites and rosés; these characteristics given by grapes with 11° of alcohol.

For the wine market, the alcohol content is the means by which the cost of the wine is assessed. Nevertheless, Rioja wine is much more than just alcohol, although they are subject to these controls.

For the new red wine 12° of alcohol can be sufficient, while a Gran Reserva red should have from 12.5° to 13.5°. A wine with 14° would have a coarse taste.

Consequently, the analysis of alcohol in wine is very important. There are several methods and it is not easy to determine the alcohol content of a wine simply by tasting it.

Generally speaking, methods are established by considering the differences between alcohol and water.

Water has a density of 1.0 and alcohol 0.793. The more alcohol present in wine, the lower its density will be, but acids, sugars and colouring matter are also present and must be separated. To do this, wine is distilled, and the acids, sugars and colouring matter are left as residues, leaving only alcohol and water. A density gauge, calibrated in degrees of alcohol is placed in this distillate and indicates the level of alcohol. This type of density gauge is called a spirit hydrometer and is a reliable and accurate device. It gives measurements to the nearest tenth of a degree.

Water has a density of 1.0; distilled wine with 12° has a density of 0.984 and one of 13°, 0.9828. These figures can only be determined by distillation.

Another method is based on the temperature at which water and alcohol boil. It is called the ebuillometric method and, although not as precise as the previous method, is of practical value. Water boils at 100°C and alcohol in wine at 76°C. The more alcohol present in wine, the lower the temperature will be at which it will boil. However, there is a slight complication; water does not always boil at 100°C. It depends on altitude and climate; at a higher temperature with high atmospheric pressure and at a lower temperature with low atmospheric pressure. The main variant is altitude; at sea level it will boil, theoretically, at 100°C. In Haro (450 m) at about 98°C. Therefore, every time this method is used, it is necessary to check the temperature at which water boils. This method does not require distillation, but cannot be used for sweet wines.

The alcohol level in wines is expressed with the symbol "°", which means degrees and separates units of tenths. It is also expressed with "G.L." , an abbreviation of the name of the French physicist Gay Lussac.

According to EEC regulations, the expression used frequently is "acquired alcohol" which is the number of degrees of alcohol which a sweet wine contains at a given moment. But there is also the expression "total alcohol" which means the degrees that sweet wine would have should its sugar also be transformed into alcohol. With regard to Rioja wines, which, with few exceptions, are not sweet, the expressions "acquired alcohol" and "total alcohol" have the same meaning.

Analysis of acidity

Grapes are an acid fruit and, consequently, wine is an acid drink.

Grapes form numerous acid substances, which are common in the world of fruit. The main acids present in grapes are as follows:

Tartaric: the prototype of acid in grapes. Can exist up to 7 g/kg in ripe fruit.

Malic: this is the typical acid of the apple. Green grapes contain a large amount but, when ripe, have very little.

When grapes ferment, these acids are transferred to the wine; in addition, other beneficial acids are formed, as well as some undesirable ones:

Lactic: this is the acid taste in yogurt and is beneficial.

Succinic: this is also beneficial.

Acetic: this is the acid contained in vinegar and is undesirable. Good wine processing should produce a minimum of acetic acid.

The acidity in wine is not usually expressed in terms of the content of each acid, but as the sum of all acids and with reference to the most important of these, which is tartaric.

Thus, the total acid content of a wine is calculated and expressed as tartaric acid. This concept is total acidity, which, in Rioja, is usually:

White . . . . 5-8 g/l
Rosé. . . . . 5-8 g/l
Young red . . . . 3-5 g/l
Matured red . . . . 5-7 g/l

This determination however does not only indicate only good acids but also includes undesirable ones such as acetic acid. As this acid can be evaporated, it is called a volatile acid. Therefore, volatile acid is undesirable and should be kept to a minimum.

The rest of the acidity, which is called fixed acidity, is favorable.

We have three concepts of acidity.

Total acidity which is the sum of fixed acidity and volatile acidity.

Volatile acidity ranges between 0.2 g/l and 1 g per litre in Rioja wines. It is not noticeable on the palate until it has a presence of more than 1 g per litre. The normal values are:

| | Values in g/l | | | |
	New	After 1 year	After 3 years	After 10 years
White	0.2	0.3	0.35	—
Rosé	0.2	0.3	0.35	—
Young red	0.15	0.5	0.7	—
Matured red	0.3	0.4	0.45	0.6

These are normal levels in wines of 11° to 13° of alcohol. In the case of higher alcohol levels, volatile acids are higher.

Generally wines have always been evaluated according to a positive factor, the alcohol content; and a negative factor, volatile acidity. This does not occur in areas which produce quality wines, where numerous other factors intervene.

The reader might wonder if acetic acid is an undesirable component and is volatile, why wine is not racked in order to release it. The answer is simply that acetic acid is volatile, but less so than alcohol. If we air it intensely, we would lose more alcohol than acetic acid.

The levels shown are normal in wine-making and conservation, but a wine in cask or bottle can be kept inadequately due to excessive temperatures, thereby increasing its volatile acidity.

There is no efficient or legal method for removing acetic acid from wine. Therefore it is necessary to be extremely careful to make sure it does not increase, either in processing or ageing.

The levels of fixed acidity are the difference between total and volatile acidity.

Volatile acidity is expressed in grammes of acetic acid per litre and total acidity in tartaric as well as fixed acidity. For this reason, in order to subtract these levels, it is necessary to determine beforehand the equivalent of acetic acid in tartaric in order to make a homogeneous subtraction. If a red Rioja wine has a total acidity of 5.4 and a volatile acidity of 0.4, to calculate the fixed acidity it is necessary to take into consideration that 0.4 in acetic acid is equivalent to 0.5 in tartaric, and, as these are homogeneous, the difference, fixed acidity, is 4.9.

According to their fixed acidity, Rioja wines may be used for different purposes. We refer to reds; whites and rosés are always more acid.

In young wines, if their fixed acidity is lower than 4.5 g/l, they will be used as young wines of the vintage. If they have between 4.5. and 5.5, they can be aged and between 5.5 and 7, they can be submitted to ageing over a long period. All this in case of wines with a alcohol level not lower than 12°.

Malic acid in grapes gives wine a disagreeable astringent taste, this is tolerable, to a certain extent, in whites and rosés, but not so in reds. For this reason, the techniques used, take advantage of a natural process caused by microbes, called malolactic deacidification. This transforms the malic acid contained in wine into lactic acid, making the wine much more pleasant on the palate. This is fermentation by bacteria which takes place after the main, or vigorous fermentation. It is considered as being a secondary fermentation. For malic acid, a very simple analytical method is used for determining when it has disappeared, and has been be converted into lactic acid.

Analysis of dry extract

In the analysis of wines there is an interesting concept known as dry extract which expresses the amount of dissolved matter which does not evaporate. This extract consists of components such as:

Fixed acids	3-10 g/l
Glycerine	4-7 g/l
Residual sugar	1-2 g/l
Natural sugar	0.5-2 g/l
Minerals in grapes	1-2 g/l

This comes to a total of 20 g/l in white wines, 22 g/l in rosés and 25 g/l in reds. It is a very important concept; wines which have low amounts of these substances are insipid and have little taste, and when in excess, are of average quality.

It is very simple to determine the amount of dry extract and two methods are available. One method, which is simple and accurate, consists of evaporating an amount of wine and weighing the residues left after the wine has evaporated completely at 100ºC.

The other system is indirect and is based on the fact that, of the three basic groups of components of wine (water, alcohol and dry extract), water has a fixed density of 1, alcohol has a fixed density of 0.793 and the extract, being dissolved, raises the density of the wine proportionally. Therefore, by knowing the density of a wine and its alcohol level, we know the density which it would have if it only consisted of water and alcohol; the value of the extract is known by means of the density of the wine. These calculations are made with a table and are very simple. The density of wines is easily determined by means of aerometry, when the wine is placed in a test tube. A density gauge, an aerometer is inserted with a stem graduated in density from 0.98 to 1.0.

Logically, these measurements have to be made at an extremely accurate temperature as volumes, therefore densities, vary with expansion or contraction. An important component of the extract is the glycerine present in wine. Grapes do not have glycerine; this is formed naturally during fermentation. It is normal for 3 to 5 g/l to be formed, but in good red wines of La Rioja, the amount which is formed can reach 7 g/l.

The density of Rioja wines is nearly 0.994, which means that the wine contained in a cask of 225 litres does not exceed 224 kg.

The more alcohol a wine has the lower its density will be.

The values for dry extract vary widely and may be as follows:

Extract	In white wine	In rosé wine	In red wine
16 g/l	Very light wine	—	—
18 g/l	Very light	Very light wine	Very weak
20 g/l	Normal	Very light	Without "body"
22 g/l	Acceptable	Little "body"	Light
24 g/l	"Heavy"	Normal "Heavy"	Acceptable in old wine
26 g/l	—	—	Normal
28 g/l	—	—	Normal in young wine
30 g/l	—	—	Normal in very young wine
32 g/l	—	—	Coarse wine
34 g/l	—	—	Sweet or "pressed", not acceptable

This data is only applicable to the typical wines of the Rioja, and not to sweet wines.

Analysis of colour

The substances which produce the natural colouring of wines can be analysed alone, separately or altogether, with a perception similar to that analised by sight.

For overall analysis, a spectrophotometric apparatus is used. Formerly, this consisted of simple colour gauges. The principle of their operation is simple: they measure the amount of light which passes through the wine. The more colour a wine has, the less the proportion of light which will pass through. Hence this involves a light source which sends light to a photometer. An exact amount of wine is placed between them, generally with a thickness of one centimeter.

Daylight is not normally used; one needs light which can be controlled with more accuracy. Therefore, this must be monochromatic and opposite to the colour which one wishes to control.

White wines only have a yellow colour, but reds and rosés have red and yellow. In order to control the yellow colour an opposite colour, blue, is used, and to control red, a green light source. Technically, these lights are defined by their wavelength, i.e., blue has a wavelength of 420 and green, 520.

Whites are measured only with light with a wavelength of 420 and reds with 420 and 520.

The more light absorbed the greater the wine's colour. This is expressed as a figure which is the sum of the light absorbed by a wine. In general terms this can be expressed for a wine with a thickness of 1 cm in a quartz tank as follows:

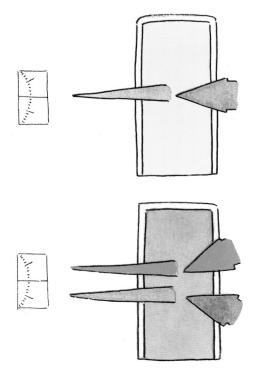

Measurement of colour in white wine. The measuring light is blue, which can absorbed by the yellow colour in the wine.

	Colour
Water	0.00
Very pale white wine	0.03
Pale white wine	0.05
Straw-coloured white wine	0.07
Golden white wine	0.1
Very golden white wine	0.15
Rosé wine with little colour	0.2
Normal rosé wine	0.3
Highly-coloured rosé wine	0.5
Strongly-coloured rosé wine	1
Red wine with very little colour	1.5
Red wine with little colour	2
Very old red wine	3
"Lágrima" red wine of wine-producers	3.2
Reserva red wine	3.3
"Medio" one year red wine of wine-producers	3.5
Matured red wine	3.7
Destemmed red wine of the year	4

This data expresses the amount of colour. However in rosés and reds it is also necessary to represent the quality of the colour, i.e., its tone. This is achieved by considering data on the absorbance of light at 420 and 520, separately and without adding them up. When wine is young, red predominates over yellow. The 420/520 ratio is less than 1. If wine is very old, yellow predominates over red and the ratio exceeds 1.

In the jargon used in laboratories, we talk of colour at 420 and at 520, meaning yellow (controlled by blue light) and red (controlled by green light).

HOW CAN ONE DISTINGUISH
A RIOJA WINE?

As wines fetch high prices on the market, one might suspect the existence of some cases of fraud. The control of Rioja wine is the responsibility of the Appellation of Origin and its Regulating Council. They impose a system of numbered labels placed on the back of the bottles, avoiding the risk of fraud. Nevertheless, it is desirable for the consumer to attain sufficient knowledge to be able to demand optimum quality.

The main characteristics of wine are derived from the types of grapes used, the type of soil and climate; as well as from technical aspects. Therefore, speaking of red Rioja wine, the main characteristic which determines the quality is the red Tempranillo grape.

Below, we offer some notes for tasting red wine from the Rioja, taking into account traditional analytical methods.

1. On removing the cork from the bottle, Rioja wine can be consumed immediately, without having to air it, or remove the cork some time before.

2. There are no unpleasant or neutral aromas. They are lively and fruity in wines of one to three years old and have a more natural "bouquet" in the case of older wines. These young "fruity" aromas and mature "bouquets" can be combined in wines of two and three years old. The taste of oak is not, and never should be, dominating.

3. To the sight, the wine shows a persistent brilliance, no sediment in the bottle, and has a balance between red and yellow tones, definable as ruby red.

4. To the palate:
   Gradual smooth impression or slightly acidic.
   Smooth impression on the gums.
   Smooth impression on the tongue or slightly acidic.
   Very smooth aftertaste, which can be described as velvety.

As the reader will note, these expressions avoid similitudes such as vanilla, leather, roses, etc., and tend to define wines by sensations to sight, smell and taste, and which can be represented graphically on the winetasting card.

In order to identify the white and rosé wines of La Rioja, it is also necessary to refer to the special characteristics of the vines which produce each kind of wine. In the same way that red wine is identified with Tempranillo, white wine is associated with the Viura grape and rosé with Garnacha.

Although La Rioja has been defined as a region which produces red wines of high quality, it should be borne in mind that fine whites and rosés are also produced.

The Viura grape provides a fruity floral aroma, good acidity, pale colour and flavours with a certain "body", without losing the finesse. In other regions, the acidity may be more pronounced and the sensation of "body" less evident.

The difficulties of differentiation are also due to the Rioja producing classical whites with a certain amount of ageing power and about 12° of alcohol, as well as "modern" light and very aromatic whites. In addition, there are producers who ferment the wine in barrel and age on the "lees". In spite of all the variations, Rioja white wine can be distinguished by a slight sensation of sweetness on the palate which corresponds to components of the Viura grape, rather than sugar.

The characteristic which differentiates rosé wine can be judged by the sensation of "body", suggesting the presence of sugar (not shown by analysis), and a very agreeable, fresh aroma as well as an apperance which tends towards an "onion skin" colour.

A new type of rosé wine has now appeared in the Rioja, based on the Tempranillo grape. It is a rosé with a tone which is less red than the traditional rosés, perhaps even a delicate shade of violet, very aromatic and with the typical structure which is a characteristic of Rioja wine.

Desks for blind tasting.

HOW CAN ONE TELL THE AGE OF A RIOJA WINE?

Basically, the age of a wine is revealed by its colour. As has been stated before, all wines have a common colour - yellow; rosés and reds also have a red component.

With maturation, the yellow component increases and whites become golden. A white must obtained from slight pressure produces pale wine. The scale of years and colour is as follows:

> First year: pale.
> Second year: straw-coloured.
> Third year: golden.
> Fourth year: very golden.
> Fifth year: maderised colour.

Colour, therefore, gives us an idea of age. However there are important secondary aspects in aroma and on the palate. Wine in the first year, in addition to having a pale colour, smells of grapes. If it is very young, it should feel "petillant" on the tip of the tongue, as it still contains carbon dioxide gas.

With respect to rosés, the colour of these wines evolves in a special way: The red decreases with time and the yellow increases.

> First year: pink.
> Second year: "onion skin".
> Third year: "oil-like".

The aroma of young rosés is also very fruity and produces the same "petillant" sensation due to the presence of CO_2 gas.

Reds offer more difficulties. Although the red colour decreases over the years and the yellow increases, with maturation over a great number of years the difficulty is greater than estimating the age of whites and rosés. It is necessary to include the concept of the vintage.

Should all vintages be the same, we would see a clear, gradual decrease in red and increase in yellow over a period of one to twenty years. It would be simple in this case for a winetaster to estimate the age of a red wine. The difficulty arises from an increase in colour from the oxidation of the yellow components being different in each vintage. Simultaneously, the decrease in the red colour does not occur at the same speed in red wines from different years. For example, a wine of the 1981 vintage today (in 1990) has a younger colour than one of 1982. In these cases, it is necessary, when winetasting, to have a chart of Rioja vintages. By relating the impression of colour, palate and aroma to the official classification, we can form our judgement of the vintage. The following may be used as a general guideline:

> First year: purple.
> Second year: red.
> Third year: ruby red.
> Fourth year: yellowish red.

Old and young wines.

Young white wine, rosé, aged red and Gran
Reserva red.

1890-1990:
ONE HUNDRED RIOJA VINTAGES
(Updated in 1996)

In southern wine-producing areas, wines of homogeneous quality are achieved year after year; light and rainfall are usually constant over the years.

On the other hand, in marginal areas such as the Rioja, quality can attain very defined characteristics; in some years superb wines can be obtained. But the climate in marginal areas is very complex and therefore the quality of the wines is sometimes extremely variable. For example, we might mention the case of Haro, lying in the heart of the area beside the River Oja, and at the centre of the Rioja. Statistically Haro produces figures for average alcohol levels in its wines at 12°, while in 1972 they only achieved 7° and in 1981, 14.5°.

Occasionally, climatic conditions coincide giving rise to grapes with strong colour, fixed acidity and alcohol level, resulting in excellent quality. These are the great vintages or "millesimes" (as expressed in French).

There is a relationship between quantity, quality and climate which is not straightforward but has interesting aspects. The following data shows the year, quality, quantity, vegetative cycle and spring frosts.

We understand the term vegetative cycle as a period with an average temperature of above 10ºC. Normally, this occurs from April 1st to October 15th and consists of 195 days. The longer this period lasts, the greater the possibility of producing a harvest of excellent quality.

The most important conclusions are as follows:

I. The best quality vintages produce high quantities of grapes and poor quality vintages mean low yields. Examples of the best are the 1964, 1985 and 1989 vintages.

II. There is no pattern in the appearance of excellent harvests. We can deduce that there does not seem to be any truth in the popular invocation of "change in climate" and that we are entering a "golden age". Vegetative cycles are increasing in length and this means better quality. From 1970 to 1980 there were few excellent harvests. As of 1980, quality has improved generally and it is difficult to name a bad harvest year. Perhaps the harvest of 1984 was not ideal, but in no way was it as poor as harvests of the previous decade.

←
A well-aged wine, requires periodic tasting during the ageing process.

SYNTHESIS OF DATA OF THE REGULATING COUNCIL OF THE APPELLATION OF ORIGINE OF LA RIOJA, MANUEL RUIZ HERNANDEZ AND JOAQUIN DE ENTREAMBASAGUAS, CARRIED OUT BY MANUEL RUIZ HERNANDEZ.

1890	VERY GOOD	
1891	MEDIOCRE	
1892	GOOD	
1893	VERY GOOD	Very low yields.
1894	EXCELLENT	
1895	VERY GOOD	Good ripening except for Garnacha.
1896	DEFICIENT	"Green" wines due to insufficient ripening. The Rioja Alavesa, can be considered GOOD.
1897	EXCELLENT	In general, wines with very good colour.
1898	EXCELLENT	Perfect ripening in the Rioja Alavesa.
1899	VERY GOOD	Wines with high fixed acidity.
1900	MEDIOCRE	Poor ripening.
1901	VERY GOOD	Balanced wines.
1902	GOOD	Moderate alcohol and low fixed acidity.
1903	GOOD	Low yields.
1904	VERY GOOD	Very balanced wines. In Haro, high alcohol level.
1905	VERY GOOD	Low yields.
1906	EXCELLENT	Very good balance between high alcohol and acidity.
1907	VERY GOOD	Violent storm in Haro in July. High alcohol level.
1908	MEDIOCRE	Production generally very low. Hail storm in August. Wines with low alcohol level. In the Rioja Alavesa, GOOD. Frosts in April.
1909	GOOD	Very low yields per hectare of Tempranillo. Mildew and oidium attacks. Frosts in May and wet August.
1910	MEDIOCRE	Very deficient ripening. Heavy frosts in April. Very wet August.
1911	MEDIOCRE	Mildew attack in August. Snow in April. Hail storm in Haro on June 8th. Hot, wet summer. 194-day cycle.
1912	DEFICIENT	Deficient ripening. Cold spring about 0º C. Dry summer and rainy September.
1913	GOOD	Tempranillo poor in acidity. Low production. Heavy frosts in April. Dry July.
1914	MEDIOCRE	Very bad flower fertilization. Few grapes and poor ripening. Very dry summer.
1915	MEDIOCRE	Mildew attack. In the Rioja Alavesa VERY GOOD quality. Dry summer and rain only in September.
1916	MEDIOCRE	Poor ripening of Tempranillo. 220-day cycle. Abnormal leaf growth in April. Dry summer, cool September and hot Autumn.
1917	GOOD	
1918	GOOD	
1919	VERY GOOD	Very good ripening.
1920	EXCELLENT	Wines with high alcohol and intense colour.
1921	GOOD	Heavy oidium attack. Strong easterly winds.
1922	EXCELLENT	Very well-balanced wines. High yields.
1923	MEDIOCRE	In the area specifically around Haro, GOOD.
1924	EXCELLENT	High yields per hectare.
1925	VERY GOOD	High yields per hectare.
1926	DEFICIENT	Tempranillo excellent in Haro. Very low yields overall.
1927	DEFICIENT	Heavy mildew attack.
1928	VERY GOOD	210-day cycle. Winds predominantly from the North-East. Frosts during harvest. Tempranillo with very low acidity.
1929	MEDIOCRE	Irregular wines, some very good. Excellent ripening of Tempranillo. High production.
1930	DEFICIENT	Deficient ripening. High production.
1931	VERY GOOD	Wines with high alcohol. In some areas more than 15º.
1932	MEDIOCRE	Low alcohol. Mildew attack.
1933	MEDIOCRE	Very irregular wines, with moderate alcohol. Low yields.
1934	EXCELLENT	Alcohol level not very high, but very well-balanced wines. Yields per hectare very high.
1935	VERY GOOD	Very well-structured wines with high alcohol.
1936	MEDIOCRE	Very low alcohol. Mildew attack. Low yields.
1937	MEDIOCRE	Low alcohol level. Extreme drought. High yields.
1938	DEFICIENT	Irregular harvest. In some areas, the wine was very good.
1939	MEDIOCRE	High yields per hectare. 190-day cycle. Moderate alcohol. Mildew attack.
1940	MEDIOCRE	Low yields. Mildew attack.
1941	GOOD	Moderate yields. 530 l/m.² of rain during the year. Spring frosts.
1942	VERY GOOD	210-day cycle. Annual rainfall of 476 l/m.². Wet summer. Wines with high alcohol and strong colour.
1943	GOOD	High yields. Annual rainfall of 410 l/m.². Wet summer.
1944	GOOD	215-day cycle. July and September cool. August hot. Little rain but very well distributed.
1945	DEFICIENT	205-day cycle. Frosts in May and very cool August. Low, badly-distributed rainfall.
1946	MEDIOCRE	205-day cycle. Cold Summer. Badly-distributed rainfall, heavy in April.
1947	VERY GOOD	210-day vegetative cycle. Hot Summer and very low annual rainfall. Extreme drought during cycle.
1948	EXCELLENT	205-day cycle. Preceding winter warm. Some frosts in spring. Rainfall was scarce but strategically, 25 l/m.² fell in August. Cool Summer.
1949	VERY GOOD	205-day cycle. Very cold May. Hot Summer. The heavy rainfall in August and September brought on a mildew attack.
1950	MEDIOCRE	200-day cycle. Frosts in April and cold September, with poor ripening. Very rainy June.
1951	MEDIOCRE	215-day cycle. Preceding Winter warm. Frosts in April and heavy mildew attack.
1952	EXCELLENT	212-day cycle. Cool July. Very hot August. Well-distributed rainfall, but dry August.
1953	DEFICIENT	205-day cycle. Heavy frosts in April. Cold June. Very hot Summer.
1954	GOOD	205-day cycle. Frosts in April. Prevailing westerly winds. Cool summer.
1955	EXCELLENT	195-day cycle. Frosts in April. Well-distributed rainfall during cycle.
1956	GOOD	175-day cycle. Preceding winter very cold and spring frosts.
1957	MEDIOCRE	210-day cycle. Preceding winter extremely cold and dry. Very wet June.
1958	EXCELLENT	188-day vegetative cycle. Prevailing westerly winds. Rainfall not excessive, 410 l/m.², very well-distributed (100 l/m.² falling in summer, was very beneficial).
1959	VERY GOOD	200-day vegetative cycle. Frosts in spring and cold June. Widely distributed rainfall during vegetative cycle, although low during budding and plentiful in September.
1960	GOOD	Volume of wine, 133 million litres. 180-day vegetative cycle, cut short by spring frosts. Very dry year. Heavy rain during harvesting. Strong winds from the south.
1961	GOOD	The harvest produced 71 million litres of wine. 207-day cycle. Strong influence of southerly winds on ripening, a hot, wet summer. Warm autumn.
1962	VERY GOOD	Volume: 124 million litres. Preceding winter very wet and not excessively cold. No frost in spring. Hot and moderately wet summer.
1963	MEDIOCRE	Volume: 109 million litres. 190-day vegetative cycle. Heavy spring frosts. Grapes were in good condition but unripe before fermentation. Preceding winter cold. In Haro there were frosts in April.
1964	EXCELLENT	For some, the best vintage of this century. Volume: 135 million litres, when the average from 1960-1970 was only 100 million litres. Excellent and plentiful. 210-day vegetative cycle, including a month of June which was relatively cold and one day of frost in April. Prevailing winds from West and North. The rainfall was 460 l/m.², but although scarce, some fell in July and August. We cannot avoid having a subjective point of view of this vintage since we were lucky enough to carry out intensive studies of the vineyards in Haro during this period.
1965	DEFICIENT	Volume: 109 million litres. 190-day vegetative cycle. Preceding winter mild. Heavy drought with prevailing westerly winds. During the period May-August (four months) only 38 l/m.² of rainfall was recorded.
1966	MEDIOCRE	Volume: 98 million litres. Month of February warm, followed by frosts in March. May and July saw abnormally cold temperatures. 200-day vegetative cycle. Prevailing westerly winds and mildew attack.
1967	MEDIOCRE	Volume: 94 million litres. 205-day vegetative cycle. Heavy spring frosts in March and April which greatly affected Rioja Alta and Rioja Alavesa. Very dry year for the vines; the rain arrived after the harvest. Hot summer.

1968	VERY GOOD	Volume: 89 million litres. 210-day vegetative cycle. Cold April. August moderately cold. Summer cool.
1969	MEDIOCRE	Volume: 85 million litres. 205-day cycle. Heavy rain in spring and September. Winds prevailing from the north.
1970	VERY GOOD	Volume: 113 million litres. 195-day vegetative cycle. Preceding winter cold and wet. Late budding. There were no spring frosts. Summer hot and wet. Some hail in June. Autumn mild with very late leaf-fall.
1971	BAD	Volume: 55 million litres. 202-day cycle. Preceding winter very cold and very dry. Very wet spring. Some frost in May. Mildew attacks. Very dry summer and ripening period. October mild.
1972	BAD	Volume: 98 million litres. 192-day vegetative cycle. Late budding in very cold weather. Summer cold. Heavy mildew attack.
1973	GOOD	In our opinion, VERY GOOD. Volume: 128 million litres. 180-day vegetative cycle. Preceding winter cold and dry. Absence of frost in the spring. Our weather station did not record appreciable rainfall. Very irregular rainfall during cycle. Hot summer.
1974	GOOD	Volume: 130 million litres. Very short vegetative cycle, of only 170 days. Preceding winter very cold, with rainfall of 130 l/m.². Heavy rain at beginning of spring. No records of frost. Hot, dry summer.
1975	VERY GOOD	Volume: 84 million litres. 185-day vegetative cycle. Preceding winter very dry (60 l/m.²). Late budding. Wet spring. Hot Summer. Harvest during very hot weather. Heavy attack of Botrytis on white grapes.
1976	GOOD	Volume: 93 million litres. 180-day vegetative cycle. Preceding winter cold and dry (only 90 l/m.²). Very cold March. Late budding. Summer wet and hot. Difficult ripening and irregular quality depending on area.
1977	MEDIOCRE	Volume: 66 million litres. 200-day vegetative cycle. Adverse conditions for vines. Spring frosts were not heavy but were persistent, followed by very heavy rain and a cold summer, although the autumn was mild.
1978	VERY GOOD	Volume: 78 million litres. 193-day vegetative cycle. Preceding winter cold and somewhat wet (130 l/m.²). Frosts in April, which ruined 20 days of the vegetative cycle. Dry summer and autumn. The wines of this vintage, twelve years later, are EXCELLENT.
1979	MEDIOCRE	Volume: 140 million litres. 210-day vegetative cycle. Preceding winter mild and wet. Absence of frost in the spring. Due to the favorable weather, good quality wine was expected until August. Later the prevailing winds changed to the East and South. Strong rainfall influenced the ripening stage producing wines of unstable colour.
1980	GOOD	Volume: 141 million litres. 192-day vegetative cycle. Absence of spring frosts. Summer cool and wet. Ripening with moderate temperatures. Wines with moderate colour but little body.
1981	VERY GOOD	We do not agree with this official classification and consider it EXCELLENT. Volume: 135 million litres. 228-day vegetative cycle. Preceding winter cold and wet (130 l/m.²). Frosts in April, first with cold winds and then with snow. First fortnight in June hot and second very cold. Up until then, bad conditions for quality but a hot autumn helped to compensate for this.
1982	EXCELLENT	Volume: 125 million litres. 210-day vegetative cycle. Preceding winter mild (115 l/m.²). Budding in hot weather. First week of July with very high temperatures. July and August had moderate rainfall (18 l/m.²). In September, 40 l/m.².
1983	GOOD	Good wines in general. Volume: 108 million litres. 216-day vegetative cycle. Preceding winter cold (150 l/m.²). Slight frost in spring. Hail in May in the area of Nájera, Cenicero and Lapuebla. Abnormal rainfall of 190 l/m.² in August. At the end of September, morning dew damaged leaves in Abalos, Baños, Elciego and Lapuebla. Harvest picked in hot weather. Wines with strong colour.
1984	MEDIOCRE	Deficient wines in certain areas. Volume: 107 million litres. 210-day vegetative cycle. Preceding winter mild and wet. Frost on May 13th in Rioja Alta and Rioja Alavesa. Hail storm on September 4th in Villalba, Briñas, Labastida. Loss of 250 tons due to hurricane "Hortensia" on October 4th. Late harvest. Cool fermentation. Sound wine of little colour.
1985	GOOD	Unusual harvest. Volume: 170 million litres. 188-day vegetative cycle. Psychologically, a weak harvest was expected and the amounts produced had not been equalled before 1992. Very good wines in high areas. Late harvest. Difficult fermentation due to the accumulation of grapes. EXCELLENT quality in Rioja Alta.
1986	GOOD	Volume: 120 million litres. 195-day vegetative cycle. There were heavy frosts in April and the summer was dry but not hot. The rainfall during the year was only 255 litres, compared with an average of 450.
1987	VERY GOOD	Volume: 133 million litres. 200-day vegetative cycle. There was slight frost in May. Preceding winter was typically cold and the summer warm. A very continental climate. The summer, besides being warm, was dry, and throughout the year only 286 litres of rainfall, compared with the normal 450.
1988	GOOD	Volume: 131 million litres. 198-day vegetative cycle. Preceding winter mild. Excess rainfall in spring and beginning of summer. 795 litres fell during the year. Consequently, mildew attacked, but was successfully fought off in La Rioja. Cool summer. Very maritime climate.
1989	GOOD	Volume: 164 million litres. Irregular ripening: very rapid until the beginning of September and then slackened. Viura fertilized very badly, giving few grapes and, consequently, early ripening. On the other hand, Tempranillo was late. White wines were not very light and the reds were of good quality in general. Carbon dioxide maceration has reacted very well in the Villalba-San Vicente-Samaniego area. The Garnacha variety in the Rioja Baja was surprising as it exceeded 16 degrees of alcohol on ripening. Reds are of a quality similar to 1985.
1990	GOOD	Quantity 161 million litres. Today we can classify the wine in cask as VERY GOOD. 195 days vegetative cycle. Very dry year with total rainfall at 365 litres from an average of 450. A vintage distinguished today (1996) for its body and smoothness.
1991	VERY GOOD	Quantity 154 million litres. Today in cask this vintage appears more descrete than 1990. Sporadic attacks of "acarus". Irregular rainfall. In late ripening zones rain interfered with the harvest giving unstable colour. Total 393 litres.
1992	GOOD	Long cycle of 212 days. Very high rainfall of 673 litres at inconvenient times. Heavy during the flowering provoking "millerandage" or the non fertilization of the Tempranillo grapes. Also heavy rain during the harvest from October 12th. Grapes picked early made EXCELLENT wines. Those picked after October 20th. DEFICIENT wines. Difficult harvest resulting in light coloured and unstable wines at the end of the harvest. The wines were difficult to clarify. Total volume 175 million litres.
1993	GOOD	Dry spring without frosts. Humid summer with normal average temperatures but at unusual times. August was hotter than July; usually it is the contrary. Cold September with rain during the first ten days. The rain was necessary but arrived too late in the Rioja Baja. It was beneficial in the Rioja Alta. Total volume 182 million litres.
1994	EXCELLENT	Total volume 177 million litres. Vegetative cycle 195 days. Hot, dry summer. From the "veraison" the grapes ripened very rapidly if somewhat irregularly, the sugar and acidity in advance of the colouring of the grapes. Some rain in September helping to advance the harvest date by 10 days from normal. Very healthy grapes. Early fermentations were rapid and temperatures sometimes quite high in consequence. Later fermentations were slower giving some irregular results. In the end the balance between alcohol, acidity and colour was very good. The viura grape ripened with unusually low acidity. The profile of the fermentation process was considered "meridional".
1995	EXCELLENT	Volume: 217 million litres. The previous winter had been mild. Rainfall from April to August was normal but July was wet. The weather in September favoured high quality as early ripening at the beginning of the month was followed by cool weather with rainfall which although not heavy was well distributed. Rainfall was recorded on thirteen days. October was dry and warm, indeed abnormally warm, leading to a high degree of ripening. The average temperature in October was higher than that of September. In general terms, the wines were of hihg graduation. Oenologists have been puzzled by unusual fermentations in which the "turbulent" fermentation was "slow" and the "slow" fermentation was "intense".

LA RIOJA ALTA, S.A.

A short history of
LA RIOJA ALTA, S.A.

Monsieur Vigier, first enologist at our bodega.

The early years

Towards the end of the 19th Century, European vineyards and the whole winemaking industry were stricken by a devastating plague - phylloxera. This tiny insect made its first appearance in Bordeaux in about 1870.

The owners of French wine cellars began to look for new areas to substitute their own afflicted wines. Before long they arrived in the Rioja, at that time still free of the dreaded plague. They found a region with a thousand-year-old tradition in the production of wine, but with certain shortcomings regarding modern technical facilities which could be used to age and preserve wines for several years. The region was, however, historically receptive to new cultures and knowledge. This interest in new technology on the part of the people of the Rioja led to feverish activity and our wineproducers quickly learnt the new techniques introduced by the French from Bordeaux.

As a result of this restlessness, several new bodegas sprang up. Among them was LA RIOJA ALTA, S.A.

On July 10th 1890, Don Daniel-Alfredo Ardanza y Sanchez managed to convince Doña Saturnina García Cid y Gárate, Don Dionisio del Prado y Lablanca, Don Felipe Puig de la Bellacasa y Herrán and Don Mariano Lacort Tapia to sign, in the presence of Don Vicente García Calzada, the public notary of Haro, the formation deed of the SOCIEDAD VINICOLA DE LA RIOJA ALTA. The original capital was 112.500 ptas, of which only 20% was paid up. With these 22.500 ptas an exhilarating business venture got under way in which the five founder members realised their common dream of producing high quality wines.

The bodega was situated in VICUANA, the celebrated station quarter of Haro. The land was the private property of the Puig de la Bellacasa and Ardanza families and rented to the Company. It was not until 1924 that the Company obtained full possession of the land it occupied.

However, the founding of our bodega was not the only important event to occur in Haro in 1890. That same year electric lighting was installed for the first time in Spain, in Haro and in Jerez. For that reason, and for others rather less refined, the saying "Haro, Paris and London" became popular among local wits to describe the Wonders of the World. Another popular expression of the time, still remembered nowadays as we approach our city, was "Ya llegamos a Haro, que se ven las luces" ("We're coming to Haro, you can see the lights").

However, to return to our subject, the European spirit, so talked about today, was very much alive in the Rioja and in our bodega in those early days. A Frenchman, Vigier, was brought in as technical director and soon the dominant means of production was what we now call the "classical" process. The original installations consisted of three plants which still exist as offices, a cooperage and the Vigier plant. In a separate building, was the fermentation plant where the 33 American oak fermentation vats were installed. These vats have been used to hold our grapes for the past 100 years. They are still used today, although now use is also made of stainless steel.

Only three months after the Company was formed, the first 3.500 Bordeaux casks were purchased. It has to be borne in mind that, at that time, wine was sold in its own cask. The prices of that period seem almost a joke today: a 225 litre cask, vintage 1890, including both wine and cask itself, was on sale for 200 ptas. Of course, in that first year the grapes cost 1.375 ptas. per "arroba" (25 lbs) - the equivalent of 0.13 ptas/kg.

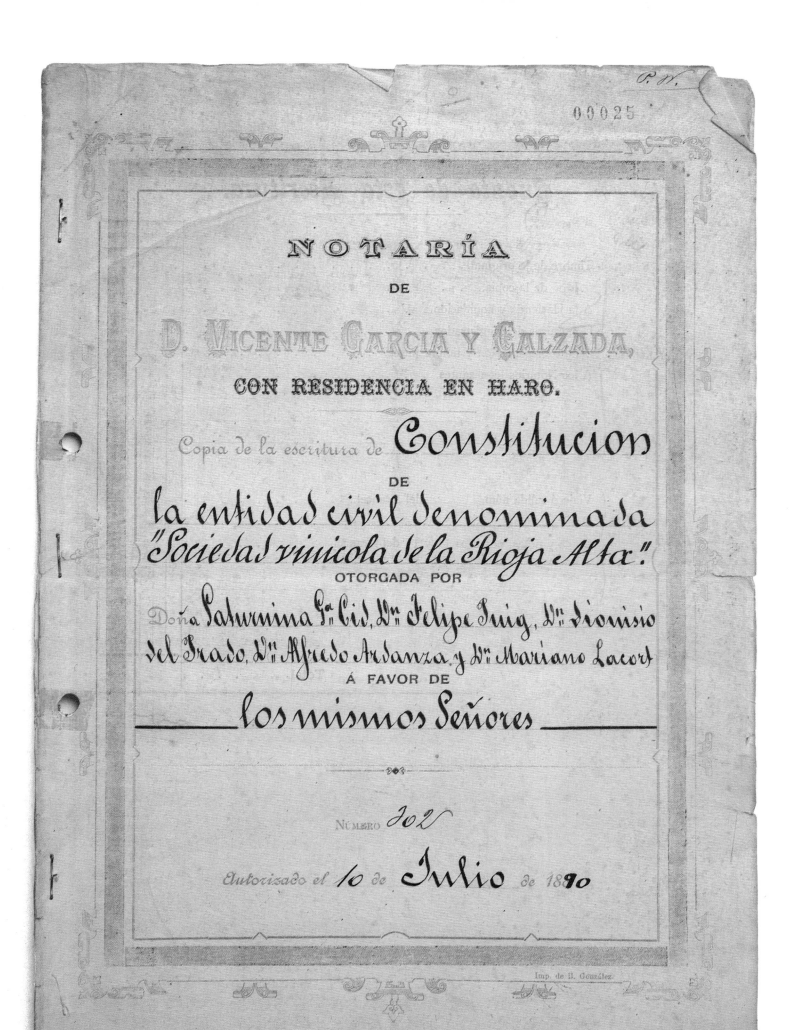

NOTARÍA

DE

D. VICENTE GARCIA Y CALZADA,

CON RESIDENCIA EN HARO.

Copia de la escritura de *Constitucion*

DE

la entidad civil denominada
"Sociedad vinicola de la Rioja Alta".

OTORGADA POR

Doña Saturnina Gª Cid, Dⁿ Felipe Puig, Dⁿ Dionisio del Prado, Dⁿ Alfredo Ardanza y Dⁿ Mariano Lacort

Á FAVOR DE

los mismos Señores

NÚMERO 302

Autorizado el 10 de *Julio* de 1890

Imp. de B. González.

A year later, on July 16th 1891, the company was renamed LA RIOJA ALTA. In 1941 the company took on the name by which it is known today, LA RIOJA ALTA, S.A.

In 1892, shortly after founding the bodega, 683,627 kgs of grapes were already being processed. But a few months later the vines were decimated by phylloxera; the enterprising vinegrowing/winemaking sector suffered a tremendous blow. Those were hard years, in which the spirit of enterprise of vineyard and bodega owners was put to the test in order to recover from the most serious crisis ever to take place in the European winemaking industry. Huge investment was necessary to recover from the consequences of the plague. The largest was the importing of American vine stocks, immune to Phylloxera, so that native vines such as "Tempranillo" could be grafted on to them. The crisis however could not last forever and our founders survived it more convinced than ever of the necessity to continue producing quality wines. It was then that the decision was taken to increase the production of bottled wine.

The first reference we have to the price of bottled wine, sold to a household in Madrid, dates from the year 1902, in which a bottle of the year 1894 (an 8-year old vintage!) was sold for 2 ptas and one of 1897 (5 years old) was sold for 1.5 ptas.

On February 26th 1892, our trademark and symbol were used for the first time. The river Oja flowing through four oak trees - it is still in use today. On September 21st 1908, this trademark was certified by the Ministry of Agriculture and renewed in 1916, as is shown at the beginning of this book.

In both Europe and America the company's wines were soon appreciated. At a time when exhibitions and competitions were so fashionable, the company achieved, among others, the following awards:

1893 - Gold Medal at the Columbus Exhibition, Chicago.

1895 - Silver Medal at the World Fair, Bordeaux.

1910 - Gran Premio, Buenos Aires.

1911 - Grand Prix, Toulouse.

1930 - Gold Medal at the Latin-American Exhibition, Seville and the Gran Premio at the Second International Congress of Vines and Wines, Barcelona.

Vendimia de 1892.
Uva ingresada.

El dia 4 Octubre			10.932
" " 5 "			34.317
" " 6 "			44.850
" " 7 "			57.398
" " 8 "			76.219
" " 9 "			67.314
" " 10 "			52.853
" " 11 "			47.835
" " 12 "			49.798
" " 13 "			33.166
" " 14 "			28.214
" " 15 "			29.341
" " 16 "			23.109
" " 17 "	32.245		3234s
" " 18 "			37.761
" " 19 "			23.000
" " 20 "			17.117
" " 21 "			12.906
" " 22 "			5.252
			683627

The first grapeharvests were made with mules.

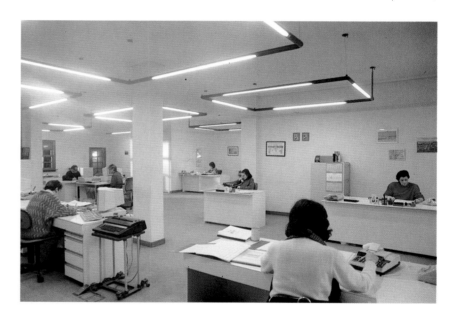

Today's offices.

All our visitors are given a good welcome to the Bodega.

Since then, it has been Company policy not to enter any kind of winetasting competition or exhibition. Although sometimes our importers and customers enter our wines.

The world of winemaking is full of tradition, classicism and respect for the past. Nowadays, this respect is kept alive by the way the grapes are processed, fermenting in the same vats that were used 100 years ago and racking by candlelight. Tradition is also guarded through the tradenames given to our wines; the majority of them have origins closely connected to our history.

In the past, the only tradename marketed was the present Reserva 890. For many years, in commemoration of the year of our foundation, it was called "Reserva 1890", but legal requirements made it necessary to drop the first figure. This also happened later with the "Reserva 1904". It would seem that, at a time when the year of production was not legally required on the label, a tradename like this caused some confusion for the winetaster especially regarding the vintage.

The first manager of the bodega was one of the founders, Don Mariano Lacort Tapia, who remained in this post until 1922, with a salary (in his first year) of 5,000 ptas. Probably one of the first management problems he had to face was how to physically export the wine to America. One must remember that, at that time, Spain had very close relations with the New World. Afterwards came the Cuban war and the loss of the colonies in 1898.

Those were years in which most wines were sold in cask and bottled by the customer at their destination, which is why for the first shipments to America the wine was sent in cask. These voyages in oak cask were of an extraordinary importance for the Rioja. It was thanks to them that notice was taken of the healthy influence of the cask on the quality of the wines. Thus it was something so seemingly unimportant as the means of transport that became a determining factor for the future of Rioja wines. It had a direct influence on their ageing process and in achieving their present quality.

Tradition would have it that it was also at the beginning of the century, when the vineyards were afflicted by the tragedy of phylloxera, that the term "Reserva" ("Reserve") came into use. It is said that, due to the scarcity of wine at the time, Frenchmen used to leave pitchers of wine in establishments they frequented, asking them to be kept in "reserve" until their next visit. Whether it be fact or fiction, this idea of a wine, being especially "reserved" is what now defines the "Reservas" of the Rioja.

In 1904, Don Alfredo Ardanza, founder of La Rioja Alta and also owner of "Bodegas Ardanza" (the Ardanza Wine Cellar), proposed the merger of both companies, a proposition which was unanimously agreed upon. To celebrate this special occasion, which happened to coincide with one of the best harvests in the history of the Rioja, a very special wine was marketed, called "Reserva 1904". Today this wine, now called "Gran Reserva 904", is one of the most delicate and complex red wines of all those under the Rioja Control of Origin.

The two "Gran Reservas 890 and 904" were offered originally in sealed bottles protected by straw and packed in wooden boxes. Years later wiring was added to these bottles. The wire netting, like sealing wax, acted as a protective seal to prevent unscrupulous persons from falling to the temptation of changing the contents of the bottle for others of inferior quality and then reselling it. Nowadays the wiring is used for aesthetic reasons and to maintain a link with our past which we have no wish to lose.

In the past everything was different, even moderation in drinking. Tasio, the company's official racking expert at the beginning of the century, used to say that he "only drank four swigs a day". Ah, but each swig was four mouthfuls and each mouthful a pint. That made a total of about eight litres!

Racking was also different. The casks were lifted by hand. At the end of a stack of casks a landing was created where the stacker rested. Thus, work continued, little by little, until five rows had been formed. Wooden rails were put in place along which the casks were rolled and lifted into position.

It was hard, physically demanding work, but it was the only method known in the Rioja for many decades. Until, in the mid-fifties, Don Carmelo Hernando, a man from Haro, invented the cask loader, with a complicated system of counterweights. This was one of the first applications of "high technology" in the bodegas of Haro.

Tasting room.

The period between the wars

From the end of the First World War until the end of the Spanish Civil War the bodega went through a quiet period with no significant changes.

In the years immediately after the 1914 War, wine was sent by rail in hogsheads to our agents, whilst a team of 4 or 5 employees from the bodega (Pedro Palacios, Estefanía, "Piedra",...) would go from agent to agent bottling the wine, capsuling it, labelling it, etc. In the bodega we still have the special, unlimited mileage season tickets they used to travel more economically. They would travel for several months at a time before returning home, making journeys throughout the whole of Spain.

In 1922, after 32 years in his position, the manager was succeeded by his son Don Mariano J. Lacort Tolosana, who held this same post for another 16 years.

In the thirties it became standard practice for bottled wine to be consigned direct from the bodega.

Although the wine was now available in bottle, it was still transported in casks, made of black poplar. The bottles of "Reserva 1890" would be placed at the bottom, wrapped in yellow cellophane paper with straw covers. The poplarwood casks, having a capacity of 100 bottles, were sent abroad, whilst for the Domestic Market the bottles were presented in the same straw covers but in wooden boxes of 24 bottles. Later the straw covers were replaced by "carenes" (papier-maché) covers and later still by pleated wrappings. Today they are sent in cardboard cartons with separators.

In 1935, under the management of Don Luis Cabezón González, the "BIKAÑA" brand was introduced, now used exclusively for the catering trade in Haro. This was done in recognition and gratitude to the city of Haro for all the support we have received during these 100 years.

In 1936, the grapes were still at almost the same price as in 1890, costing 0.18 ptas/kg, but a year later the price almost doubled to 0.34 ptas/kg. It seems logical to suppose that war-induced inflation was behind this price increase.

In 1940, Cuba was our number one client, importing especially Viña Ardanza and a 3rd year wine, predecessor to Viña Alberdi. Exports continued to rise despite our importing agent's fears that "with the 3rd year wine at 5 ptas per bottle we may lose all our customers". Nonetheless, sales increased until (as the reader may well imagine) the Cuban Revolution.

Meanwhile, in Venezuela we had a very good market. "Radiante", a semi-sweet wine, was the main attraction in that country. It was used for celebrating Mass. The situation reached such a point that to export the wine, apart from the corresponding analysis of the Enological Centre in Haro, a certificate from the Bishopric had to be arranged, recognising the suitability of the wine for Consecration.

On September 28th 1942, under the chairmanship of Don Leandro Ardanza Angulo a tradename was registered which was to become the most famous and prestigious of the company - "Viña Ardanza".

The name originated from one of the families with the closest links to the bodega. Even today Don Alfredo Ardanza, a direct descendent of Don Daniel-Alfredo Ardanza, the founder, is a director of our company. Right from the beginning Viña Ardanza has been, for its intrinsic characteristics, for its originality and personality, the showpiece and most important representative wine of our bodega.

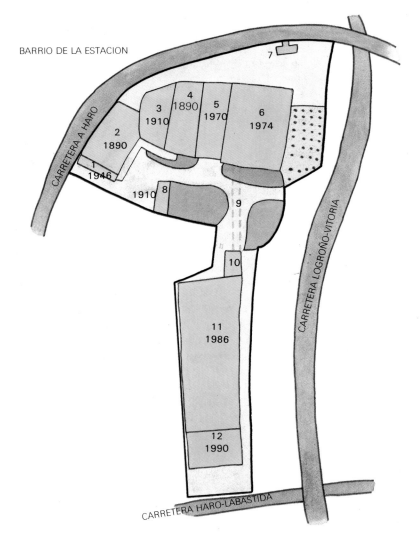

BARRIO DE LA ESTACION

CARRETERA A HARO

CARRETERA LOGROÑO-VITORIA

CARRETERA HARO-LABASTIDA

3
1910

4
1890

5
1970

6
1974

2
1890

1
1946

1910

8

9

10

11
1986

12
1990

7

1. OFFICES
   1946
2. OFFICES
   CASKS
   BOTTLE STORE
   VATS
   1890
   (2 levels)
3. BOTTLE STORE
   1910
   (2 levels)
4. VAT CELLAR
   1890
   (2 levels)
5. FERMENTATION CELLAR
   BOTTLE STORE
   BOTTLING PLANT
   1970
   (2 levels)
6. CASKS AND BOTTLE STORE
   1974
   (3 levels)
7. WEIGH BRIDGE
8. 1910
9. TUNNEL FOR BOTTLE AGEING
10. LABORATORY
11. CASK CELLAR
    1986
    (2 levels
12. CASKS
    1990
    (2 levels

195

All our investments have been made with the intention of improving the ageing and quality of our wines.

During those decades the casks were entirely made in our bodega. A team of 5 coopers were responsible for making the casks. Today, because of the large number of Bordeaux casks, our barrel-making department is scarcely involved in the making of casks; it is mainly dedicated to repairs.

Recent decades

In the mid-forties the recently-appointed director Don Nicolás Salterain Elgoibar, after 13 business trips to carry out negotiations, was able to present to the then Chairman, Don Nicolás Alberdi, the purchase of the Labastida bodega, situated in the district of La Horca. There, even today, 1,200 casks are kept with tens of thousands of bottles of "Gran Reserva" wines for ageing.

In 1946, an annex to the first plant, the bureau, which still forms part of the present-day offices, was built.

Meanwhile the directors held their regular board meetings in both Haro and Labastida. Some of the directors, like Don Pedro (wearing his famous cape) and his brother Don Paco Ortiz de Zúñiga y López de Alda, would arrive there in the old double-decker buses run by the Alavesa Company. The latter brother, chairman in 1953, was succeeded in this position by his son, Don Eduardo Ortiz de Zúñiga Montero.

In 1952, the company bought its first bottling line, the first **GIRONDINE** line in the Rioja, with a capacity of 900/1,000 bottles per hour. This machine can now be seen in the gardens of the bodega. Until then, all the wine had been bottled and corked by hand. Shortly after this Don Manuel Legorburu Bilbao became Chairman.

But times were changing as were prices. In 1965, when Don Fernando Maguregui Ulargui was chairman, the 3rd year vintage was sold at 17 ptas per bottle, the 6th year at 19 ptas, the Viña Ardanza at 22 ptas and the Reserva 904 at 40 ptas per bottle.

The old bridge of Haro has been replaced by modern roads.

In 1974, a new brand name was introduced on the market, "Viña Arana". However it was not a new wine, it was the new commercial name for the classic 6-year-old vintage. It came from the 1969 harvest. It is a fine, delicate, light wine with mild and intense aromas. The name came from the present Vice-Chairman, Don Jose María de Arana Aizpurua, and it is the type of wine that the people from Bordeaux, who worked in the Haro bodegas, called "Rioja Claret". This was to differentiate it from the so-called "red wines" normally processed from the racking of the rich wines from the lower and Navarra riversides of the Ebro river.

This wine was presented as "Crianza" or aged wine, because traditionally in the Rioja, wines were only known with or without ageing or "Crianza". The terms Reserva and Gran Reserva were introduced at a later date. Some years later, within the same decade of the 70's, "Viña Arana" became a Reserva.

In 1970, a new plant for vats was built. Since 1987, having established that stainless steel vats offered a great improvement over oak in the fermentation process (and only in fermentation), both in terms of hygiene and in temperature control, the vats in the harvesting plant have been changed for stainless steel. However we still keep the 32 original oak vats for second fermentation and storage purpuses.

Also in the 70s, the last two delegations representing the bodega, in San Sebastian and Madrid, were closed. There began a significant expansion of vineyard holding with the purchase of lands in Tudelilla (32 hectares), Montecillo (21 hectares) and Rodezno (the Viña Arana estate of 35 hectares and the Viña Alberdi estate of 22 hectares).

The expansion of the bodega and vineyars required new investments in casks, so in 1973, the land next to our original buildings was bought from Don Otto Horcher and a year later a dining hall was opened there. The same building included the cellars of "Marqués de Haro" and "Viña Alberdi". This last brand name was the substitute for the previous 3 year old vintage. It owes its name to Don Nicolás Alberdi who, as we mentioned earlier, was our Chairman in the forties. This brand name was registered in 1978, the first vintage being that of 1974. At present it is our youngest wine and the only "Crianza" wine we offer. However, it is quite possible that in the not-too-distant future, with the agreement of our enologist, we may offer it as a Reserva. It already fulfills the official requirements, but these are less stringent than the ones we impose ourselves.

Don Fernando Maguregui Ulargui, a good man and an expert administrator, had, for reasons of health, offered his resignation as chairman over some years. In 1979, his request was accepted and Don Guillermo de Aranzabal Alberdi, proposed by his predecessor, was appointed chairman, a position he has held to the present day.

Expansion, which is now culminating, began in the 70s. The reinvestment of each year's profits was not sufficient to finance our investments and we had to complement it with several increases of capital between 1973 and 1977, with premium stock reaching almost 200 million pesetas. Since 1978, and up to the present day, we have been able to finance our development ourselves.

The 80s saw an important extension of our installations and vineyards as well as the culmination of what has perhaps been the most important achievement in the bodega in many years - the definition of product. Contrary to the trends at the time, it was agreed to increase the ageing of all our wines, both in cask and in bottle. At the same time emphasis was placed on the quality of the grapes which enter the cellars and, as far as possible, self-sufficiency in this respect.

This radical stance in favour of quality demanded a very heavy investment for a family business of medium size, but all the shareholders agreed with the proposed policy and accepted the sacrifices that such an investment would mean. So in 1986 the ageing tunnel was built, as were the "Viña Arana" and "Viña Ardanza" plants, extended in 1990 to store 20,600 Bordeaux casks, bringing the total to 32,000 casks.

To better ensure the quality of the grapes and our own autonomy the "La Cuesta" estate, renamed "Viña Ardanza", was purchased. It is situated in the village of Cenicero and consists of 58 hectares, all of which are dedicated to Tempranillo.

As to the definition of product to which we referred earlier, there were also some significant changes. Some brands disappearing whilst others were introduced. One of these changes occurred in 1980 when Don Fernando Fernández Cormenzana, at that time acting manager, developed a charming idea suggested by the shareholder Don Jose Ramón de Aranzabal and promoted the creation, with a select number

of private clients, of the CLUB DE COSECHEROS DE LA RIOJA ALTA, S.A. A special wine was chosen of the 1976 vintage, offered as a Crianza wine, although the quality was gradually improved until its present status as a Reserva, along the lines of the "Clarets" mentioned earlier.

In 1985, a brandname was registered which will be much spoken of in the future - "Marqués de Haro", and in 1988 there appeared the most recent wine to be introduced by the bodega, the "Viña Ardanza Blanco", a Reserva which corresponds perfectly with our philosophy of offering only traditional Rioja wines.

At the same time the last young white wine to be offered by our cellar was abandoned and there began an earnest search for a white wine with personality, with elements to make it different from other Spanish wines. The consequence of this was the acquisition and renovation of a traditional bodega situated in the heart of Galicia, "Lagar de Fornelos, S.A.", who commercialises the "Lagar de Cervera" brand. Its 50 hectares of 100% Albariño grapes ensure maximum quality.

The early nineties have represented one of the periods of greater activity in our company due both to the favourable reception all our products have enjoyed on markets both at home and abroad, and to the wider horizons the bodega has set for its development over recent years.

In 1990 and 1991, 65 hectares were acquired within the municipalities of La Horra and Anguix in the heart of the *Ribera de Duero* region, an area which produces wines of high quality.

In 1994 and within a period of just four months, the *Botellero del Jardín* bottle cellar was built in Haro. To do so, it was necessary to excavate entirely the yard of the bodega, replace all the earth and then cover it with grass. This new bottle cellar has capacity for around 2.5 million bottles.

On January 27th 1995, we purchased a 96.33% holding in Torre de Oña, S.A., a beautiful bodega located in Páganos-Laguardia, producer of Barón de Oña Reserva red wine. With this acquisition, we intend to place ourselves among producers of some of the finest wines in the Rioja Alavesa.

In January 1996, work began on the extension to the bodega in Labastida. This work is being done on our own land and at a distance of about 1,500 metres from our main plant in Haro. This new bodega, created under the company name "Comercializadora La Rioja Alta, S.L.U.", will carry out the entire wine-making process and part of the

202

ageing process, both in cask and in bottle. This will allow us to obtain considerable improvements in quality, especially in the fermentation process, as the new bodega will be provided with state-of-the-art technology. It will also enable us to increase our production somewhat and introduce a higher level of flexibility in the ageing processes of the different vintages.

The future

These are a few details of our story, the history of LA RIOJA ALTA, S.A.

We feel sure that the original concept dating from 1890 is still present in LA RIOJA ALTA, S.A., and we try zealously to preserve the creative and enterprising spirit of our founders.

We hold our history and the philosophy of our founders in great respect, evident not only in our way of making wine but also in our brands, in our dealings with clients and in our close relations with the town of Haro.

It is also evident that, with the passage of time, LA RIOJA ALTA, S.A., without losing sight of the aim for maximum quality outlined at its very foundation, is continually expanding installations and vineyards, totalling at present (including the extension in Labastida), 44,000 American oak casks for the preparation of wines, more than 8.6 million bottles of wine in the process of ageing and more than three hundred hectares of the best vineyards. The 19 million litres we hold in vat, cask and bottle are the equivalent to more than eight years' sales. Besides the vineyards we have already mentioned, those worthy of note are: Labastida (8 hectares), Briones (10 ha), Fuenmayor (31 ha), El Cortijo (18 ha), Zarratón (8 ha) and another 60 hectares in various villages in the northern part of the Rioja.

But life continues and our dedication to quality presents us with more ambitious objectives every day. Our next aim, which we will achieve within a few months, is to be the only bodega of a certain size in the Rioja to offer its customers exclusively Reservas and Gran Reservas. We are very close to achieving this aim and the challenge, exciting and difficult from many points of view, is demanding all our attention.

We are not so interested in the quantity as in the quality of our wines. We want them all to be of a high standard, which means sacrificing large and easy sales.

By means of these brief notes, these small anecdotes, we hope the reader will have been able to enter a little more into the life of our firm and will be able to better understand the aims and objectives which serve as guidelines for LA RIOJA ALTA, S.A.

Haro, 1996

THE WINES
OF LA RIOJA ALTA, S.A.

Each January, with the first racking of the recent harvest, the enologist must decide the destination of the different musts. To do this he makes use of objective analyses of the wine, such as alcohol content and acidity, and his own criteria regarding colour and taste, formed by years of dedication to his profession.

He, and he alone, must decide whether the wine from a particular vat is suitable to become a Gran Reserva or if it would be better suited to a good Crianza. For these reasons, at La Rioja Alta, S.A., we do not produce annually all the different types of wines available, rather those which are nearest to the characteristics of the harvest. In this way we can preserve the essential nature of each brand and achieve a large degree of homogeneity in its quality.

Each one of our wines has its own special identity, but they all form part of the family of wines of La Rioja Alta, S.A. There are certain features which are characteristic in them all - their delicacy, their elegance, the vanilla and oak aromas, the smooth passage through the mouth, velvety, whole...

The wines we have the pleasure of presenting here are of different vintages, different ageing, different harvests... but they all carry the unmistakable hallmark of La Rioja Alta, S.A.

Two years in wooden vats, 10 in casks of about 20 years old and 4 more in bottles, have produced the Centenary wine. Vanilla, truffle, oak. Very rounded and balanced. Unrepeatable.

La Rioja Alta, S.A.

BODEGAS FUNDADAS EN 1890

HARO

ESPAÑA

MARCA CONCEDIDA

Rioja Alta, S.A.

SOCIEDAD DE COSECHEROS DE VINO

FUNDADA EN 1890

COSECHA 1973

EMBOTELLADO EN LA PROPIEDAD

RIOJA

DENOMINACION DE ORIGEN

ENARIO 1890-1990

A hundred years of history separate these two bottles.

GRAN RESERVA 904
4 years in bottle rounds off 5 years in casks. Penetrating ruby colour with brick-red highlights. Fat and fluid. Velvety. 12.5°.

GRAN RESERVA 890
8 years in cask and 6 in bottle age a wine which is very difficult to describe. It is made only with the best vintages, selected with extreme care. Numbered bottles. 12.5°

VIÑA ARDANZA RESERVA
6-year old red, 3 1/2 years of which have been in casks, with extraordinary body, clear robe and an intense fragrance.
Balsamic and rounded aftertaste. 13°.

VIÑA ARANA RESERVA
Traditional "Rioja Claret" of the area around Haro, with 3 years in casks and 2 in bottle. Smooth, fine, elegant. Balanced. With slight acidity and a touch of vanilla, 12.°.

WHITE VIÑA ARDANZA
Dry Reserva white. Two years in cask and 1 in bottles, age a great wine for lovers of "historical" white wine. Complex aroma, clean, intense aftertaste. 12°.

VIÑA ALBERDI
Aged red. Smooth, fruity, fine with a fresh palate. Delicate bouquet, very characteristic of the Rioja, 2 years in casks and 2 in bottles. 12°.

211